THE KINGDOM

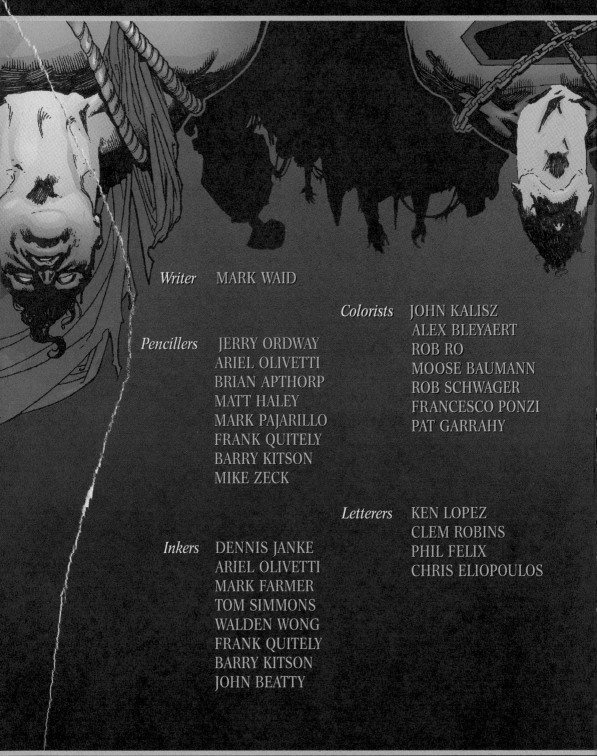

Writer   MARK WAID

Colorists   JOHN KALISZ
ALEX BLEYAERT
ROB RO
Pencillers   JERRY ORDWAY
ARIEL OLIVETTI
MOOSE BAUMANN
BRIAN APTHORP
ROB SCHWAGER
MATT HALEY
FRANCESCO PONZI
MARK PAJARILLO
PAT GARRAHY
FRANK QUITELY
BARRY KITSON
MIKE ZECK

Letterers   KEN LOPEZ
CLEM ROBINS
PHIL FELIX
CHRIS ELIOPOULOS

Inkers   DENNIS JANKE
ARIEL OLIVETTI
MARK FARMER
TOM SIMMONS
WALDEN WONG
FRANK QUITELY
BARRY KITSON
JOHN BEATTY

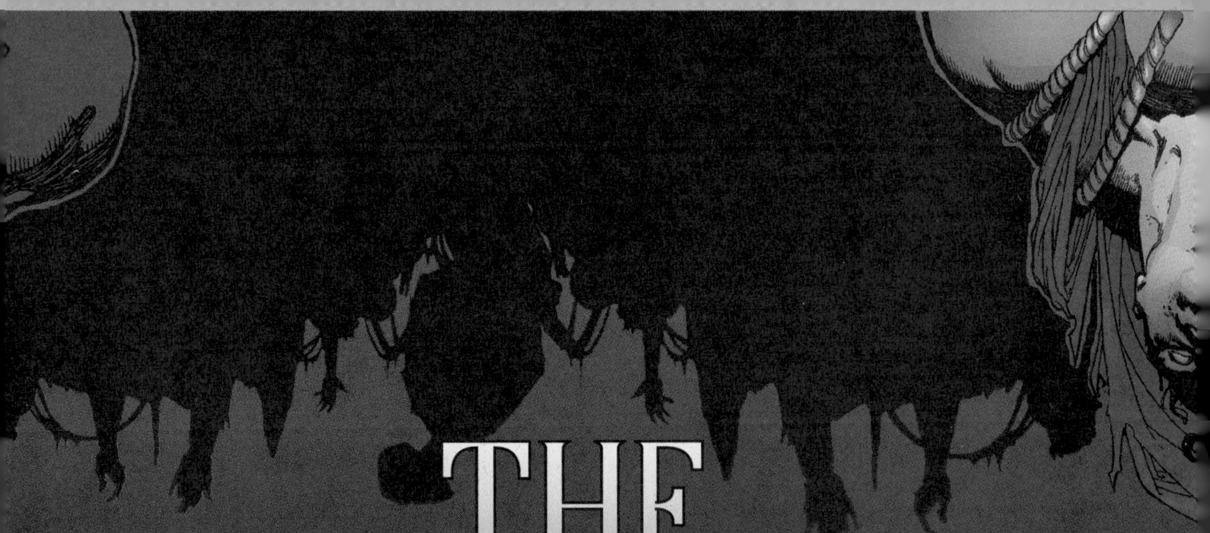

THE KINGDOM

Based on
KINGDOM COME
by
MARK WAID and ALEX ROSS

President & Editor-in-Chief	JENETTE KAHN
Executive Vice President & Publisher	PAUL LEVITZ
Executive Editor	MIKE CARLIN
Editor-original series	DAN RASPLER
Editor-collected edition	DALE CRAIN
Associate Editor-original series	TONY BEDARD
Assistant Editor-collected edition	MICHAEL WRIGHT
Design Director	GEORG BREWER
Art Director	ROBBIN BROSTERMAN
VP-Creative Director	RICHARD BRUNING
VP-Finance & Operations	PATRICK CALDON
VP-Licensed Publishing	DOROTHY CROUCH
VP-Managing Editor	TERRI CUNNINGHAM
Senior VP-Advertising & Promotions	JOEL EHRLICH
Exec. Director-Manufacturing	ALISON GILL
VP & General Counsel	LILLIAN LASERSON
Editorial Director-WildStorm	JIM LEE
VP & General Manager-WildStorm	JOHN NEE
VP-Direct Sales	BOB WAYNE

THE KINGDOM
ISBN 1-84023-122-X

Published by Titan Books, a division of Titan Publishing Group Ltd., 144 Southwark St., London SE1 OUP under licence from DC Comics. Cover, introduction and compilation copyright © 1999 DC Comics. All Rights Reserved.

Originally published in single magazine form as GOG (VILLAINS) #1, THE KINGDOM #1-2, THE KINGDOM: SON OF THE BAT #1, THE KINGDOM: NIGHTSTAR #1, THE KINGDOM: KID FLASH #1, THE KINGDOM: OFFSPRING #1, THE KINGDOM: PLANET KRYPTON #1. Copyright © 1998, 1999 DC Comics. All Rights Reserved. All characters, their distinctive likenesses and related indicia featured in this publication are trademarks of DC Comics. The stories, characters, and incidents featured in this publication are entirely fictional.

Printed in Canada. 10 9 8 7 6 5 4 3 2 1
First Edition: December 1999.

Cover illustration by Mike Zeck and John Beatty.

Cover color by Kurt Goldzung.

Publication design by Jason Lyons.

To order titles from the backlist page, please quote reference code KING/GN.

I n the future – one that may or may not come to pass – the so-called "Silver Age" of heroes came to an end. Many of its greatest legends passed their mantles to their children, successors and protégés, as they themselves either quietly retired or concerned themselves with greater pursuits. The new generation of champions, however, soon proved to be anything but as turf wars erupted between rival gangs of metahumans. These petty disputes soon led to a major disaster as Kansas – indeed, all of America's breadbasket – was laid waste as the result of a superhuman battle gone horribly wrong.

Shocked back into action by the tragedy in Kansas, Superman returned from his self-imposed exile and rallied his former Justice League allies to his side. Their mission was simple: order...at any cost. But the Man of Steel's dreams of a just world soon became the stuff of his nightmares.

Fearing the metahuman situation was already beyond anyone's control, the United Nations opted to eliminate the perceived threat – by again turning Kansas into a nuclear wasteland with Superman and the rest of the metahuman population at ground zero. When the radioactive smoke finally cleared, only Superman, the Batman, Wonder Woman and a handful of metahumans had survived the blast. But the sacrifice of their comrades was not in vain. A new environment of trust and cooperation was born as the remaining members of the League joined with humanity to once more forge a better tomorrow.

One such architect of the future to come is a young man known only as William, a survivor of the first Kansas tragedy. A man with a grand destiny he is not yet aware of, he will soon have the opportunity to either change the past for the better – or plunge the entirety of the timestream itself, as well as one of its most closely guarded secrets, into an even darker abyss...

JASON

Jason Pearson

THERE.

HE IS THE ONE.

WE ARE AGREED, THEN?

YES. HAVE WE ANY HOPE OF ALTERING THE COURSE OF EARTH'S CATACLYSMIC FATE...

...IT LIES WITH *HIM*. HE SHALL BE OUR *AGENT*.

HIS JOURNEY SHALL REQUIRE A *MAP.* WITHIN THIS *SCROLL*, WE FOUR PLACE THE *DETAILS* OF *EVERY EVENT* THAT LED TO KANSAS' DESTRUCTION...

...AND THE *POWER* TO *CHANGE* THOSE EVENTS... AND CHANGE THE *WORLD*.

AND I? WHAT SHALL MY ROLE BE?

YOU, STRANGER, WILL DELIVER TO OUR AGENT HIS TASK. HE IS NO LONGER A MERE CHILD INCAPABLE OF ACTION. WE NOW KNOW HIM TO BE AN *ADULT*...

MINISTER... WILLIAM, IS IT? MINISTER, I'M A REPORTER WITH THE *DAILY PLANET*.

I COULDN'T HELP OVERHEARING, DO YOU ACTUALLY... PREACH A *GOSPEL* BASED ON *SUPERMAN*?

I SPREAD HIS *WORD*, YES... THROUGHOUT HIS LAND.

LOOK AT IT. IT'S *MAGNIFICENT*.

THIS WONDERFUL WORLD IN WHICH WE LIVE... THIS *UTOPIA*, THIS *GOLDEN AGE*... IT IS HIS GIFT. HIS REWARD.

SURRENDER YOUR FAITH UNTO *SUPERMAN*...

...AND UNTO YOU HE WILL DELIVER.

REALLY? TELL ME *MORE.*

MINISTER, YOU'RE OLD ENOUGH TO REMEMBER A TIME BEFORE THE ENLIGHTENMENT.

IT SOUNDS AS IF YOU HAVE A RATHER UNIQUE TAKE ON THE KANSAS INCIDENT THAT *SPARKED* IT. YOUR MEMORIES OF KANSAS ARE...?

OF A GREAT SPIRITUAL *AWAKENING.*

APPROXIMATELY TWENTY YEARS INTO THE NEW MILLENNIUM, SUPERMAN TESTED OUR FAITH. HE AND HIS DISCIPLES *DISAPPEARED.*

IN THEIR ABSENCE, THE WORLD WAS OVERRUN BY *FALSE PROPHETS...*

..."CHAMPIONS" WHOSE NIHILISTIC CARELESSNESS COST THE WORLD A MILLION LIVES IN KANSAS *ALONE.*

THOSE OF US WHO *REJECTED* THEM... WHO MAINTAINED THE *TRUE* FAITH... WERE THEN *REWARDED...*

... WHEN SUPERMAN AROSE TO PULL THE WORLD BACK FROM THE BRINK OF *NUCLEAR* DESTRUCTION.

HE REMINDED US THAT WE CANNOT *ABIDE* THE VILLAINY OF *FALSE PROPHETS.* THERE IS *NO* GREATER EVIL THAN *THEIRS...*

... FOR THEY WILL *SURELY* LEAD US TO *DAMNATION.*

11

...ONLY TO BE *INSPIRED* BY HIM.

HIS WORD IS SIMPLE. "THERE IS A *RIGHT* AND A *WRONG* IN THE UNIVERSE, AND THAT DISTINCTION IS NOT HARD TO MAKE. DO RIGHT BY ALL."

WHETHER YOU *BELIEVE* IN HIS *DIVINITY* OR NOT, IT IS A *GOOD MESSAGE.* HE CHOSE ME TO PREACH IT IN THIS FAITHLESS TIME, AND PREACH IT I *SHALL.* HERE, BEGINNING *TOMORROW.*

..., I HAVE MUCH TO *ACCOMPLISH.*

SO HE'S A *NUT.*

NOT AT *ALL.* HE'S *PASSIONATE.*

MAYBE WE SHOULD ALL BE THAT *NUTS.*

IT HAS TAKEN ME A *LIFETIME,* BUT I HAVE CONSTRUCTED A HOUSE OF *WORSHIP.* I ONLY PRAY HE FINDS IT *WORTHY.*

THE MINISTRY OF WILLIAM

TELL THE *WORLD* ABOUT IT, MR...

OLSEN.

NO LANDING

OLSEN. NOW IF YOU'LL *EXCUSE* ME....

DAILY PLANET EDITOR

IT'S YOU...!

YES, WILLIAM, IT *IS*. I'VE BEEN *HEARING* ABOUT YOU LATELY.

ONLY... LATELY...?

AND I *REMEMBER* YOU. YOU'RE THE BOY FROM *KANSAS*.

"WHEN IT *EXPLODED* TWENTY YEARS AGO, THAT DREW ME OUT OF RETIREMENT. IMMEDIATELY, I WENT LOOKING FOR *SURVIVORS*. I FOUND ONLY *YOU*... WANDERING THE PERIPHERY OF THE BLAST, LOST AND ALONE.

"I DROPPED YOU OFF AT A NEBRASKA HOSPITAL ON MY WAY BACK TO METROPOLIS. YOU WERE TREATED FOR RADIATION POISONING AND EVENTUALLY RELEASED."

YOU'VE GROWN UP *WELL*. YOU DO GOOD *THINGS*.

THANK YOU.

IT WAS *YOUR* WILL.

I... I JUST DON'T UNDERSTAND WHY... AFTER A *MILLION DIED* IN KANSAS... YOU WOULD DO *THIS* IN MY NAME.

BECAUSE THEY GAVE THEIR LIVES FOR A *REASON*, OF COURSE.

YES, I SAW UNSPEAKABLE HORRORS, I LOST EVERYTHING I KNEW, I WANDERED LOST AND ALONE, AND I SURVIVED ONLY BECAUSE I REALIZED THE TRUTH.

THAT NOTHING SO CATASTROPHIC COULD HAVE OCCURRED SO SENSELESSLY.

KANSAS WAS YOUR TEST OF FAITH... AND I PASSED. THAT'S WHY YOU CHOSE ME ALONE TO BE YOUR MESSENGER. AND I HAVE LABORED HARD TO EARN THAT TRUST, SUPERMAN.

WILLIAM, I...

... I DIDN'T... CHOOSE YOU. WHAT HAPPENED TO KANSAS...IT WASN'T MY WILL, IT WAS MY FAULT.

WHAT...?

I HAD RETIRED, I'D TURNED AWAY FROM SERVING MORTAL MEN WHEN I THOUGHT THEY NO LONGER EMBRACED THE SAME VIRTUES I DID.

BECAUSE I LEFT, OTHERS WERE ABLE TO RISE TO POWER. I FAILED YOU, WILLIAM. THEY TOOK KANSAS NOT BECAUSE I WANTED THEM TO...

...BUT BECAUSE I WASN'T THERE TO STOP THEM.

MY PEERS AND I HAD PLACED OUR-SELVES ABOVE HUMANITY, AND HUMANITY LET US. AS A RESULT, THE WORLD WAS NEARLY DESTROYED BY OUR INABILITY TO WORK TOGETHER.

I'M NOT A GOD, WILLIAM. I DIDN'T SINGLE YOU OUT BECAUSE YOU'RE SPECIAL. YOU WERE LUCKY.

IT'S ONLY HUMAN TO WANT TO FIND SENSE IN A SENSELESS TRAGEDY, BUT SOMETIMES... SOMETIMES IT ISN'T THERE.

I'M NOT SPECIAL...?

EVERYONE IS SPECIAL, WILLIAM.

WE WILL NEVER MAKE THAT ERROR AGAIN, WE WILL FOREVERMORE WORK WITH YOU... WITHIN SOCIETY. THAT IS OUR VOW.

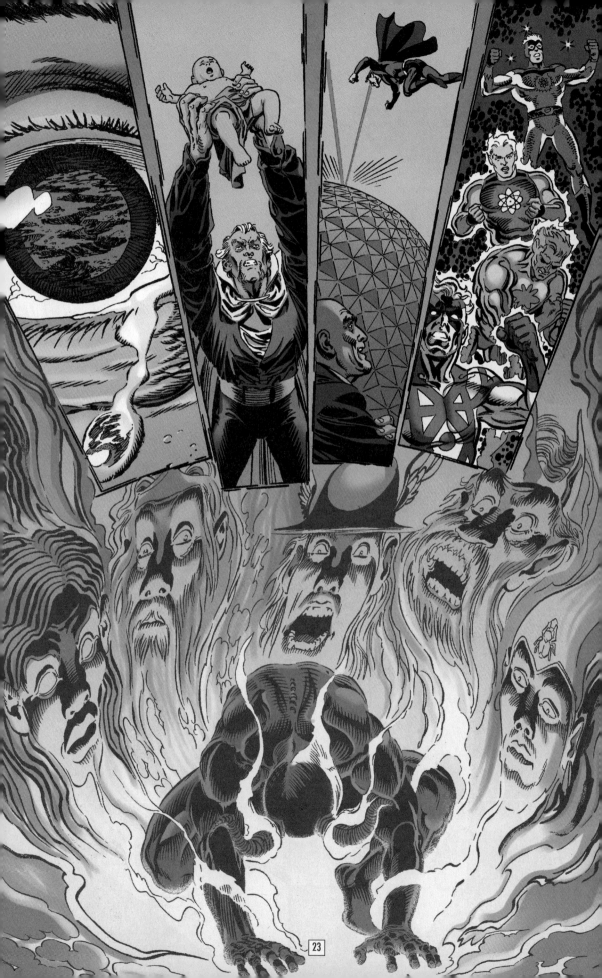

METROPOLIS TO **LONDON**, GENTLEMEN, WE'RE ALMOST **THERE**... BUT NOW WE'RE WAITING FOR GREEN LANTERN.

HE'S BRINGING THE **PROMETHIUM PYLONS** WE NEED.

UNTIL THEN, TELL THE MEN TO TAKE A **BREAK**. WE'VE WORKED **HARD** TODAY, AND--

... I KNOW THAT HEARTBEAT.

WILLIAM?

YOU'RE STILL TROUBLED, I'M GLAD YOU **FOUND** ME.

YOU'VE COME FOR... HELP? ADVICE?

YOU NEARLY *HAD ME.*

NOW I KNOW THE *TRUTH.* YOU *TRICKED* ME INTO BELIEVING YOUR *LIES,* INTO TELLING *OTHERS* THAT YOU WERE OUR *SAVIOR,* THAT YOU WOULDN'T LET EVIL *BEFALL* US.

OF *COURSE* YOU WOULDN'T.

YOU DIDN'T WANT THE *COMPETITION.*

HOW? HOW COULD I *FORGET?* WE CANNOT *ABIDE* THE VILLAINY OF *FALSE PROPHETS...* FOR THERE IS *NO GREATER EVIL* THAN THEIRS.

THAN *YOURS.*

I WAS *BLIND,* BUT NOW I *SEE.* YOU ARE THE *ULTIMATE* EVIL OF *LEGEND,* A *WINGED* CREATURE ALIEN TO US, CAST OUT OF *PARADISE* LIKE A STAR FALLING FROM THE *SKY.*

A BEING PERSUASIVE AND CHARISMATIC OF TREMENDOUS POWER, POSING AS A *GODSEND* SO AS TO SWAY MEN'S SPIRITS TO HIS TEACHINGS.

A *BEAST...*

...IDENTIFIED BY *ONE DISTINCTIVE MARK,*

28

A BEAST WHOSE SUBVERSIVE, ENDMOST GOAL IS ARMAGEDDON.

YOU WERE *CLEVER*, SUPERMAN. DESPITE YOUR *METICULOUS* PLANNING, YOU WERE ONCE *THWARTED* OF THAT GOAL... BUT, DEVIL THAT YOU *ARE*, YOU SNATCHED *TRUST* FROM THE JAWS OF *DEFEAT*.

YOU AND YOUR *DISCIPLES* FEIGNED HUMILITY IN ORDER TO *TRICK* US INTO *EMBRACING* YOU MORE FIRMLY...

...INTO *ALLOWING* YOU TO WALK *AMONG* US, AS ONE *OF* US...

...SO THAT YOU MIGHT STEER US TOWARDS OUR *FINAL END* FROM *WITHIN* EVEN AS WE *CELEBRATED* YOUR *PRESENCE*.

NOW YOU ARE *GONE*... BUT EVEN IN *DEATH*, YOUR *INSIDIOUS* TOUCH TAINTS EVERYONE AND *EVERYTHING* IN THIS REMADE *KINGDOM* OF YOURS.

TO MAKE IT *CLEAN* AGAIN, I MUST GO *BACK*... AND *EXPOSE* YOUR DARKNESS BEFORE IT TAKES *ROOT*.

I WILL SHOW THE WORLD THE DEPTH OF YOUR EVIL BY LINKING YOU *CLEARLY* TO THE CATACLYSM *YOU ALLOWED*.

YOU ESCAPED *BLAME* FOR THE HORROR OF KANSAS *ONLY* BECAUSE IT HAPPENED *AFTER YOU RETIRED*. THAT, SUPERMAN...

...CAN BE *CHANGED*.

29

SADLY... TYPICALLY... THE HUMAN MIND IS OFTTIMES IN-CAPABLE OF COMPREHENDING THE WISDOM OF THE GODS.

THIS... THIS CANNOT BE RIGHT...

IT IS ENTIRELY LIKELY THAT THE VASTNESS OF OUR KNOWLEDGE HAS TAINTED HIM WITH MADNESS.

AND SO HE HAS INTERPRETED YOUR WISDOM TO FILL THE EMPTINESS OF HIS OWN SOUL!

YOU HAVE DONE THE UNTHINKABLE! YOU'VE CREATED SOMEONE WHO HATES SUPERMAN! IF HE'S TO BE YOUR AGENT OF CHANGE, HE IS HARDLY FIT FOR THE TASK!

ON THE CONTRARY. HE IS NOW PERFECTLY EQUIPPED.

HOW? HE IS NOW AN ANGEL OF RAGE AND VENGEANCE. YOU HEARD HIM. NOT ONLY WILL HE NOT PREVENT THE TRAGEDY OF KANSAS...

...HE PLANS TO ACCELERATE IT.

EXACTLY.

THE END FOR NOW

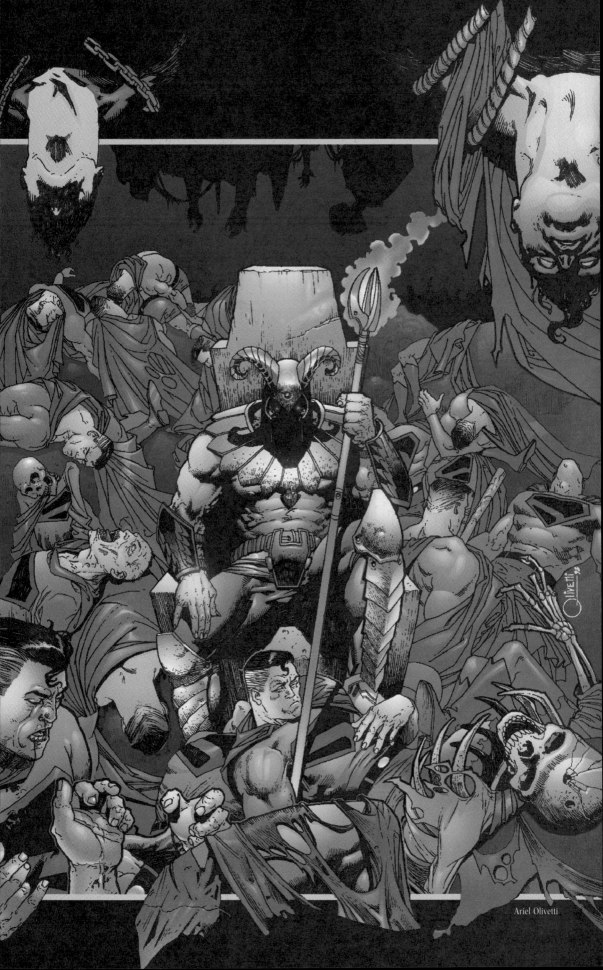

Ariel Olivetti

IF ANYONE EVER DESERVED HEAVEN, IT WAS HIM.

A BLISSFUL REWARD COMMENSURATE WITH THE GREATNESS OF HIS LEGEND. A FAMILIAR REALM NONETHELESS REMOVED FROM WORLDLY CONCERNS.

AND FOR A WHILE, THE SONG OF ANGELS MINGLED WITH HEARTBEATS OF HIS LOVED ONES AND THE CLACK OF TYPEWRITER KEYS...

...TO DRIVE A NAGGING REALIZATION FROM HIS BRAIN.

ONCE UPON A TIME, THE SLIGHTEST SQUINT HAD ALLOWED HIM TO SEE BEYOND THE STARS.

THE SMALLEST STEP HAD CARRIED HIM FROM PLANET TO PLANET.

BUT HERE, FOR THE FIRST TIME IN HIS LONG LIFE...

...THERE ARE LIMITS.

THOOM

≡SIGH≡

LIKE CLOCKWORK.

LOOK.

UP IN THE SKY.

THE   KINGDOM

OH, MAN.

OH, MANO-MANO-MAN. HOW MANY DID HE GET SO FAR? CARRY THE FOUR...

...AND SIX AND SEVEN IS...

...

... AHHH... MAYBE IT'D BE FASTER T'MULTIPLY, INSTEAD...

WHERE AM I?

≡SIGH≡

AW, GREAT. ANOTHER ONE.

DEAD-MAN? IS THAT YOU?

CHAUFFEUR TO THE AFTERLIFE, ONE AND THE SAME. WISH I COULD SAY I WAS GLAD TO SEE YA, PAL. NOW... WHAT'S TODAY?

BUT ...BUT YOU'RE A GHOST. IF I CAN... SEE YOU...

TODAY, CLARK. A LITTLE *HELP* HERE. WHAT'S THE *DATE?*

...THEN I MUST BE... *DEAD,* TOO...?

THAT'S *RIGHT.* YOU WERE *MURDERED,* CLARKIE. NOW YOU'RE A *GHOST.* SORRY TO BREAK IT TO YOU. CONDOLENCES LATER.

RIGHT NOW, I GOTTA KNOW THE DATE YOU *DIED.* STAY WITH ME, HERE.

SNAP!
SNAP!

"... JULY 10TH...?

YEAR?

2031.

OKAY. THAT CHECKS. WE'VE BEEN *EXPECTING* YOU.

C'MON. LET ME TAKE YA TO THE *OTHERS.*

OTHERS? WHO *ELSE...?*

OH, YOU'RE IN GOOD *COMPANY,* PAL.

ALLOW ME TO INTRODUCE YOU AROUND, MR. JULY 10TH, 2031.

SEPTEMBER 19TH, 2038.
MARCH 21ST, 2033.
DECEMBER 24TH, 2022.
OCTOBER 9TH, 2027.
WELCOME TO THE CLUB.

NEVER ENDING SLAUGHTER

MARK WAID
WRITER

ARIEL OLIVETTI
ARTIST

PHIL FELIX
LETTERS

JOHN KALISZ
COLORS

CHRIS CHUCKRY
SEPARATIONS

TONY BEDARD
ASSOCIATE ED.

DAN RASPLER
EDITOR

BASED ON *KINGDOM COME* BY MARK WAID AND ALEX ROSS

SUPERMAN CREATED BY JERRY SIEGEL AND JOE SHUSTER

"THE EXPLOSION OF KRYPTON."

YOU MIGHT WANT TO THANK ME.

THIS TIME, I DIDN'T KILL YOU.

NOT IMMEDIATELY, ANYWAY.

OH, YOU'LL DIE, ALL RIGHT... BUT NOT BEFORE YOU SPEND THE NEXT THOUSAND YEARS SCREAMING...

...EVERY CELL IN YOUR BODY TRANSFORMED INTO *LIVING KRYPTONITE!*

SOME VIEW FROM UP HERE, HUH? SORRY, MAN.

EVERY...DAY. THIS "GOG"... HE'S MARCHING BACK THROUGH TIME...KILLING ME ANEW EVERY SINGLE DAY!

HE CAN'T DO THAT!

IT'S A SHOCK, I KNOW. DENIAL'S A NATURAL STAGE. ROLL WITH IT...

NO! I MEAN IT'S NOT POSSIBLE! I DON'T ACCEPT THIS!

THE NATURE OF THE TIME PARADOX... MURDERING ME EARLIER AND EARLIER THROUGHOUT MY LIFE...

...BY EVERY RULE WE KNOW, THE SPACE-TIME CONTINUUM OUGHT TO BE HEMORRHAGING CHAOS!

AND YET, IT'S NOT. DON'T ASK ME. I JUST WORK HERE. 'SIDES, I'VE GOT TO GET YOU SPIRITS MOVING UPWARD AND ONWARD.

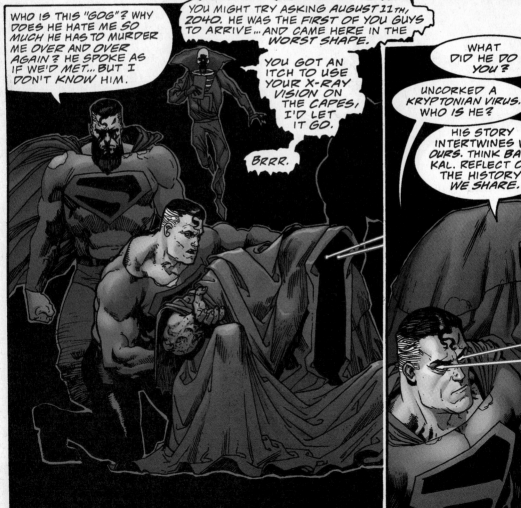

WHO IS THIS "GOG"? WHY DOES HE HATE ME SO MUCH HE HAS TO MURDER ME OVER AND OVER AGAIN? HE SPOKE AS IF WE'D MET... BUT I DON'T KNOW HIM.

YOU MIGHT TRY ASKING AUGUST 11TH, 2040. HE WAS THE FIRST OF YOU GUYS TO ARRIVE... AND CAME HERE IN THE WORST SHAPE.

YOU GOT AN ITCH TO USE YOUR X-RAY VISION ON THE CAPES, I'D LET IT GO.

BRRR.

WHAT DID HE DO TO YOU?

UNCORKED A KRYPTONIAN VIRUS. WHO IS HE?

HIS STORY INTERTWINES WITH OURS. THINK BACK, KAL. REFLECT ON THE HISTORY WE SHARE.

"IN THE FIRST DECADE OF THE *TWENTY-FIRST CENTURY,* THE WORLD BEGAN ANSWERING TO A *NEW BREED* OF YOUNG HEROES.

"AT FIRST, WE *WELCOMED* THEIR HELP...UNTIL WE REALIZED JUST HOW *DIFFERENT* THEY WERE.

"*MISGUIDED...RUTHLESS...* SOME, BORDERLINE *PSYCHOTIC...* THEY GRABBED THE MORAL COMPASS OUR GENERATION HAD ESTABLISHED AND GAVE IT A NASTY SPIN...

"EVENTUALLY, AFTER YEARS OF TRYING TO *CONTROL* THEM...OF WATCHING HELP-LESSLY AS CITIZENS CHEERED THEM ON, *RE-JECTING* THE VIRTUES WE'D STOOD FOR...

"...WE AND OUR *FRIENDS* LEFT OUR RESPONSIBILITIES TO *THEM.*

"IT WAS THE GREATEST *ERROR* IN JUDGMENT WE COULD HAVE *MADE.*

"WITHOUT *US* TO HOLD THEM IN *CHECK,* THEY WENT *WILD.* IN TIME, THEIR ACTIONS PREDI-CATED A NUCLEAR DISASTER THAT CLAIMED THE ENTIRETY OF KANSAS.

"THAT'S WHAT BROUGHT ME...*US...* OUT OF *RETIREMENT.* IN ALL THAT *DEVASTATION,* WE FOUND ONLY ONE *SURVIVOR...A YOUNG BOY* WHO'D LOST EVERYTHING. HIS NAME WAS WILLIAM."

I REMEMBER. WHATEVER *BECAME* OF HIM?

LOOK.

"HE BECAME A MINISTER...

"...WHO HAD A RATHER UNIQUE CONCEPT OF GOD'S IDENTITY.

"THE SENSELESSNESS OF THE KANSAS DISASTER HAD DRIVEN WILLIAM TO THE BRINK OF MADNESS.

"HE CONVINCED HIMSELF KANSAS WAS MY TEST OF FAITH...JUST FOR HIM. THAT I WAS A HOLY BEING, AND I'D SELECTED HIM TO BE MY MESSENGER.

"WHEN I FOUND OUT AND TOLD HIM WHAT HAD REALLY HAPPENED...HOW WE'D SINNED BY DISTANCING OURSELVES FROM HUMANITY... HOW KANSAS WASN'T MY WILL, BUT RATHER MY FAULT...

"...WILLIAM CREATED A NEW TRUTH.

"I WAS THE ANTI-CHRIST."

"SOON AFTER, A CONCLAVE OF COSMIC IMMORTALS KNOWN AS THE QUINTESSENCE TOOK ADVANTAGE OF WILLIAM'S RAGE. ELECTING THE PHANTOM STRANGER THEIR MESSENGER..."

"...THEY CONFERRED UPON WILLIAM IMMEASURABLE KNOWLEDGE AND IMMENSE POWER..."

"...WHICH HE USED TO END MY LIFE..."

"...THE FIRST OF A THOUSAND TIMES."

GOOD GOD. HOW CAN ANYONE KNOW SUCH ANGER?

I WISH IT WERE JUST ANGER... BUT IT'S STRATEGY, AS WELL. HE WANTS TO MAKE CERTAIN THERE'S NO SUPERMAN ANYWHERE WHO CAN STOP HIM. THE QUINTESSENCE GAVE HIM A MISSION, KAL...TO CHANGE HISTORY.

TO ACCELERATE THE KANSAS DISASTER AND ALL THE TRAGEDY WHICH FOLLOWED...

BUS IS PULLIN' OUT, BOYS. LET'S GO. WE GOT MORE COMIN' IN EVERY MINUTE.

WHY WOULD ANYONE WANT KANSAS TO HAPPEN SOONER?

AN EXCELLENT *QUESTION*...

...WHICH ONLY THE *QUINTESSENCE* CAN ANSWER.

IF THE *KANSAS* DISASTER HAPPENS *SOONER*, ZEUS, BEFORE THE SUPER-HUMANS RETIRE, MORTALS' FAITH IN THEM MIGHT BE *FOREVER SHATTERED*.

PERHAPS THEIR NEED TO BELIEVE IN SOMETHING WILL FAVOR THE NEARLY FORGOTTEN *OLYMPIAN GODS*.

IF IT HAPPENS *SOONER*, GANTHET, PERHAPS YOUR *GREEN LANTERN* OF THE LATE 20th CENTURY CAN STOP IT--

--GIVING YOU INFLUENCE OVER A *CHAMPION* WHOSE GALACTIC STATURE WOULD THEN ECLIPSE *SUPERMAN'S*.

IF IT HAPPENS *SOONER*, HIGH-FATHER, PERHAPS THE WAR BETWEEN HUMANS AND SUPER-HUMANS IT SPARKS WILL GIVE YOU WHAT YOU WANT.

PERHAPS THIS TIME, THE BATTLE'S *EXPLOSIVENESS*, WOULD FISSION THE *GOOD* ON EARTH SAFELY AWAY FROM THE *EVIL*--

--JUST AS A SIMILAR GODWAR DIVIDED NEW GENESIS AND APOKOLIPS EONS AGO.

IF IT HAPPENS *SOONER*, WIZARD SHAZAM, PERHAPS YOUR *BELOVED BILLY BATSON* WILL NOT HAVE TO *DIE* TO STOP IT.

PERHAPS. PERHAPS!

HOW *DARE YOU* PLAY *DICE* WITH HUMANITY'S FATE TO FAVOR YOUR OWN ENDS? HAVE YOU LEARNED NOTHING?

IN YOUR "INFINITE WISDOM," YOU HAVE FALLEN PREY TO THE SAME ARROGANCE WHICH *BEGAN* THIS CALAMITY!

LIKE THE SUPERHUMANS, YOU HAVE POSITIONED YOURSELVES *ABOVE* THOSE WITH WHOM YOU SHARE THE UNIVERSE--

YOU SPEAK THAT WAY TO ME? SURELY I CANNOT BE HELD ACCOUNTABLE FOR THE ACTIONS OF *THEIR* AGENT!

OUR AGENT, GANTHET. YOU WERE AS RESPONSIBLE FOR HIS CREATION AS THE *REST* OF US.

WE CHARTED A SPECIFIC *DESTINATION* FOR HIM. HARDLY OUR FAULT THAT IN HIS RAGE HE HAS CHOSEN A RATHER GRUESOME *PATH.*

PERHAPS THE GIFTS OF GODLY WISDOM AND POWER WERE TOO MUCH FOR A POOR MORTAL TO BEAR.

SO. YOU HAVE *PITY* FOR WILLIAM.

HOW TOUCHING. THE GALACTIC POWERS HAVE FOUND SYMPATHY FOR A MORTAL MAN... *TOO LATE.*

I *ACHE* TO LEAVE YOUR COMPANY, TO SET THIS *RIGHT*... BUT I *DARE NOT.* I HAVE NO CHOICE BUT TO *MONITOR* YOU FOUR TO MAKE CERTAIN YOU TAKE NO ACTION TO *COMPOUND* THIS CRISIS.

STILL, I MUST *ACT*... AND, IN ALL OF TIME AND SPACE, THERE IS ONLY *ONE* BEING WHO CAN WORK AS MY *AGENT.*

"ONLY ONE WHO KNOWS THE SUPREME AND UNWHISPERABLE SECRET THAT GOG'S ACTIONS MAY SOON EXPOSE."

HUNTER!

HUNTER, DON'T *TOUCH* THAT! FOR THE LAST TIME, THE PROBLEM'S NOT IN THE *CHRONO-SANDS!*

WHAT IS *WRONG* WITH THIS *INFINI-TRACKER?*

SORRY, LIRI. GUESS THIS *ANOMALY'S* GOT US ALL FLUSTERED.

"ANOMALY," HE CALLS IT. TRY "*CATASTROPHE.*"

HUNTER, FORGIVE US, BUT WE HAVEN'T THE *PATIENCE* RIGHT NOW TO TOLERATE YOUR *NAIVETÉ!*

WE STAND ON THE BRINK OF *ARMAGEDDON!* EVERY TIME THIS "GOG" SLAYS A VERSION OF SUPERMAN *YOUNGER* THAN THE *LAST* ONE HE MURDERED--

--HE TAKES A *SLEDGE-HAMMER* TO THE *SPACE-TIME CONTINUUM!*

THERE'S NO *TELLING* HOW MUCH HE'S *ENDANGERING* ALL REALITY-- ALL *EXISTENCE*-- NOT WITHOUT OUR *EQUIPMENT* WORKING PROPERLY!

WHEN I FIRST BEGAN *INVESTIGATING* THIS PARADOX, I THOUGHT A SIMPLE *EXPLORATION* BEYOND THE *TIME BARRIER* WOULD CLEAR IT UP.

AND WHAT DID YOU *SEE* THERE?

... MADNESS. CHAOS. OBVIOUSLY, I WAS CAUGHT IN A *HALLUCINATORY* GRIP -- BUT I'M ALL *RIGHT* NOW. I KNOW WHAT'S *REAL* AND WHAT'S *FALSE.*

IN FACT... I *DEFINE* IT.

WE ALL DO! WE'RE THE LINEAR MEN, FOR GOD'S SAKE! IT'S OUR JOB TO KEEP THE CONTINUUM ON ITS ONE TRUE PATH--

--TO MAINTAIN CONTINUITY--

--AND YET, OUR INSTRUMENTS ARE SUDDENLY PROVING USELESS IN GIVING US ANY SORT OF READING ON THIS AT ALL!

THEY CAN'T FIND ANY ANOMALY.

A GOOD CARPENTER NEVER BLAMES HIS TOOLS.

WHAT?

NOTHING.

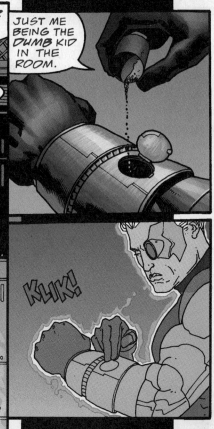

JUST ME BEING THE DUMB KID IN THE ROOM.

KLIK!

WE HAVE TO BEND MORE TIME, PEOPLE! WE'VE SPENT A MONTH INVESTIGATING THIS TODAY-- AND WE'LL SPEND A YEAR THIS WEEK IF WE HAVE TO!

THIS IS YOUR AGENT, NOW ACTIVE. I HAVE TARGETED GOG AND AM ON MY WAY TO CONFRONT HIM ON THE ONE PAST-DAY AVAILABLE TO ME.

HAVE WE CHECKED THE MOBIUS ENGINE? HUNTER, CAN YOU HELP ME WITH THAT?

HUNTER? WHERE ARE YOU?

THERE...IN ORDER TO CONCEAL MY ACTIONS FROM THE LINEAR MEN, I MUST SEAL OFF A TIMEPOINT-- AN UNDETECTABLE SHIELD AROUND THE ONE DAY IN HISTORY--

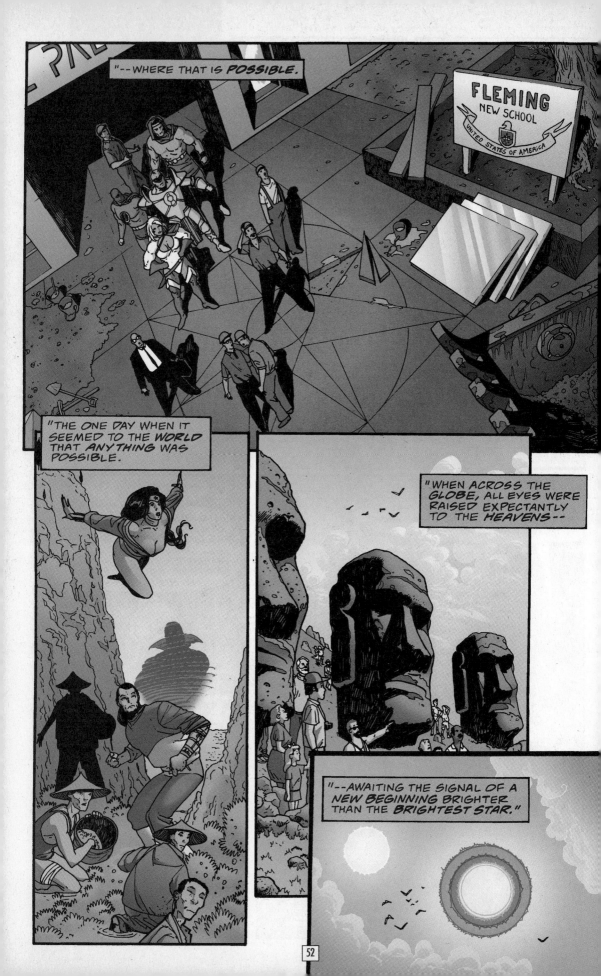

"--WHERE THAT IS *POSSIBLE*.

FLEMING
NEW SCHOOL
UNITED STATES OF AMERICA

"THE ONE DAY WHEN IT SEEMED TO THE *WORLD* THAT *ANYTHING* WAS *POSSIBLE*.

"WHEN ACROSS THE *GLOBE*, ALL EYES WERE RAISED EXPECTANTLY TO THE *HEAVENS*--

"--AWAITING THE SIGNAL OF A *NEW BEGINNING* BRIGHTER THAN THE *BRIGHTEST STAR*."

UNGH!

AAAAAAH!

THAT'S IT, HONEY. BREATHE. BREATHE AND *PUSH.*

HOW'S SHE DOING, CLARK?

CLARK? I *HEARD* YOU, BRUCE. DIANA'S *FINE*, FRANKLY, I WAS *WORRIED* THAT THE AMAZONS OF PARADISE ISLAND MIGHT HAVE FORGOTTEN *HOW* TO MIDWIFE AFTER ALL THESE YEARS--

--BUT THEY'VE BEEN *TERRIFIC*, I, ON THE OTHER HAND, FEEL *RIDICULOUS--*

--ESPECIALLY WITH A *MICROPHONE* AT MY THROAT. YOU'RE THE CHILD'S GODFATHER, BRUCE...

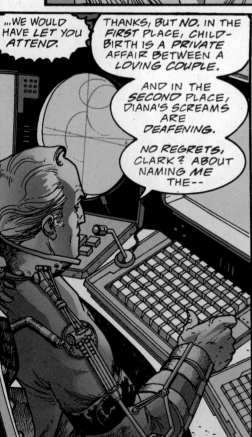

...WE WOULD HAVE *LET* YOU ATTEND.

THANKS, BUT *NO.* IN THE FIRST PLACE, CHILD-BIRTH IS A *PRIVATE* AFFAIR BETWEEN A LOVING COUPLE.

AND IN THE SECOND PLACE, DIANA'S SCREAMS ARE *DEAFENING.*

NO REGRETS, CLARK? ABOUT NAMING ME THE--

WE *TALKED* ABOUT THIS, BRUCE. HE--OR *SHE*--WILL BE AS MUCH *YOUR* CHILD AS *OURS*, OLD FRIEND.

IN THIS WORLD, MARTHA--OR *JONATHAN*--WILL NEED *HUMAN* GUIDANCE AS WELL AS *SUPER-HUMAN.* JUST BE CAREFUL WHAT YOU TEACH HER.

OR *HIM.* HOW ARE *YOU* HOLDING UP?

I'M WALKING ON AIR. I--

ME?

NNNNNUHHH!

=GASP=

CLARK...?

OH, MY GOD, DIANA...

...HE'S BEAUTIFUL.

HELLO, JONATHAN.

HELLO, MA.

THIS JUST IN, STARMAN:

IT'S A BOY... HALE AND HEALTHY...

...WHICH SOUNDS LIKE OUR CUE.

RAY--FATE-- READY?

SISTERS-- TO ARMS! OUR PRINCESS NEEDS US!

YEAAARGH!

NOT REALLY.

I KNOW WHAT YOU'RE *THINKING*, SUPER-MAN. AFTER ALL THE *TIMES* WE'VE MET... HOW COULD I *NOT?*

BUT WERE I YOU--

--I'D HOLD MY FIRE.

HOW IS IT POSSIBLE I KNEW NOTHING OF THIS LITTLE HELLSPAWN URCHIN?

WHY IS THAT?

WHO... WHO *ARE* YOU...?

WAH WAH WAH

NOOOO!

MY NAME IS GOG...

...AND I AM *RETRIBUTION* MOST *DIVINE.*

57

RETRI... ...RETRIBUTION...?

YOU USED ME, SUPER-MAN. I SURRENDERED MY FAITH UNTO YOU... AND IN DOING SO, COMMITTED MY SOUL TO A FALSE GOD.

...TO PREACH YOUR WORD... BUT I DID NOT SEE YOU FOR WHO YOU TRULY ARE.

YOU ARE THE ULTIMATE EVIL. THE FALLEN, WINGED ANGEL CAST OUT OF PARADISE LIKE A STAR FALLING FROM THE SKY.

...WILLIAM...?

YOU PULLED ME FROM THE ASHES OF KANSAS...

NYAAAGH!

THE BEAST OF HOLY LEGEND... IDENTIFIED BY ONE DISTINCTIVE MARK.

ON THE CORPSES OF A MILLION INNOCENTS... OF MY MOTHER, MY FATHER... MY CHILDHOOD... YOU BUILT A DECEPTION OF BIBLICAL PROPORTION.

IT IS MY MISSION TO EXPOSE YOU... GUIDED BY THE ONLY TRUE WORDS WHICH EVER SPILLED FROM YOUR VILE LIPS.

I ALONE KNOW YOUR SECRET. THAT YOU ALLOWED THE KANSAS CATACLYSM TO UNFOLD SO THAT YOU COULD "FIX" IT...SO THAT YOU COULD POSE AS HUMANITY'S SAVIOR.

THERE IS A RIGHT AND A WRONG IN THE UNIVERSE...

...AND THAT DISTINCTION IS NOT HARD TO MAKE.

CLARK, IF YOU CAN STILL *HEAR* ME, IT'S *BRUCE.* I'VE DISPATCHED THE CAVALRY AND I'M ON MY *WAY.*

LET THE *OTHERS* HANDLE THIS *MADMAN.* YOU STAY WITH--

DIANA!

RELEASE MY *BOY!*

THWAM!

UNLIKELY. YOU'RE A WARRIOR, WONDER WOMAN.

SURELY YOU KNOW THE BATTLE VALUE OF A *SHIELD.*

I HAVE A CLEAN SHOT--

NIGHTSTAR, *NO!* YOU'VE SEEN HOW *FAST* HE IS! HE CAN PUT THAT BABY BETWEEN HIM AND US AT THE SPEED OF LIGHT! TO MAKE THE *RESCUE*--

--WE NEED SOMEONE EVEN *FASTER*--!

ANYTHING.

THEN SACRIFICE YOUR INSTINCTS-- AND STAY BACK.

LOOK OUT!

AAARGH!

HE'S LIKE AN ARMY OF SUPER-MEN--!

NO ONE'S BOTHERED TO CLOCK GOG'S SPEED ...BUT IF I USE THE POWER OF THESE WRIST-BANDS TO STEP BETWEEN NANOSECONDS, I HAVE TO BE FASTER THAN HIM.

IN HIS MADNESS, GOG COULD STILL SNAP YOUR CHILD IN HALF BEFORE WE CAN RESTRAIN HIM. ONCE I GET THE BOY...

KLIK!

"...I HOPE YOU KNOCK HIM TO SATURN AND BACK!"

64

KSSSH!

LANTERN!

≡GNNNGGH!≡

HE'S NOT BREATHING! GET HIM OUT OF HERE!

BE CAREFUL! THE BABY'S PROTECTION'S BEEN SHATTERED!

NOT SO FAST.

I BELIEVE THESE WRIST-BANDS ARE THE DEVICES WHICH MAINTAIN YOUR "TIME BARRIER," ARE THEY NOT?

WERE THEY NOT?

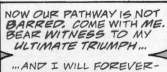

KRUNKZZKT!

NOW OUR PATHWAY IS NOT BARRED. COME WITH ME. BEAR WITNESS TO MY ULTIMATE TRIUMPH...

...AND I WILL FOREVER-MORE PROTECT YOU FROM YOUR FATHER'S EVIL.

YOU ARE SAFE WITH ME, LITTLE ONE. WE ARE, IN OUR WAY, BROTHERS... CHILDREN OF THE DARK-NESS, CHAMPIONS OF THE LIGHT.

AS I AM GOG...

...SO SHALL YOU BE MY MAGOG...

NOOOO!

--WILL CEASE TO EXIST.

I'M *SORRY.* IT'S UN-FAIR. EVEN IF YOU *WIN,* YOU *LOSE.* SO FRAGILE IS THE *GOSSAMER* OF DESTINY.

GOG INTENDS TO DESTROY KANSAS PRE-MATURELY. WHETHER HE SUCCEEDS AT THAT OR NOT, HE CANNOT *HELP* BUT ALTER ALL THAT IS FATED TO FOLLOW.

SHOULD YOU INTRODUCE *YOURSELVES* INTO THE EQUATION-- ENCOUNTER YOUR 1998 SELVES, TELL THEM WHAT YOU KNOW--WE CANNOT SALVAGE THE COURSE OF EVENTS WHICH HAS GIVEN YOU THE WORLD YOU KNOW. EARTH'S ONE, TRUE TIMELINE WILL *REMOLD* ITSELF, ERASING *ALL YOU HOLD DEAR...*

...INCLUDING YOUR NEWBORN SON.

ARE YOU PREPARED TO SIGN THE **DEATH WARRANT** FOR YOUR WORLD?

CLARK? ARE YOU... ARE YOU ASKING **US?**

WE... DON'T KNOW...

DON'T WE?

OUR WORLD DESERVES TO **LIVE**... BUT SO DO THE PEOPLE OF 1998 KANSAS.

SOUNDS TO **ME** LIKE PEOPLE WILL **DIE** NO MATTER **WHAT'S** DECIDED... SO...

...SO... ALL THINGS BEING **EQUAL**... WE ACT LIKE **HEROES.**

THAT'S ALL WE CAN DO.

YOU TAUGHT US THAT.

WE COMMEND YOUR NOBILITY... BUT THIS ISN'T UP FOR A **VOTE.** THIS--

HUNTER? HUNTER, WHAT ARE YOU **DOING?**

KLIK!

AGREEING WITH THE **GIRL.**

LET'S GO, YOU **THREE.**

Brian Apthorp/John Beatty

CONVERGENCE

MARK WAID-writer   BRIAN APTHORP-pencils
MARK FARMER-inks   KEN LOPEZ-letters
ALEX BLEYAERT & ROB RO-colors & seps
TONY BEDARD-assoc editor   DAN RASPLER-editor

Based on
KINGDOM COME
by MARK WAID
and ALEX ROSS

BLEEP
BLEEP

GIBSON 2102

rmmMM

MORNIN', DOC. HOW'S THE *PRESIDENT* TODAY?

PATIENT-DOCTOR CONFIDENTIALITY *ASIDE*, SAM...HE'S JUST *FINE*. SHUT THE *DOOR*?

I'VE HAD A MINOR *SETBACK*.

LOST MY PERSPECTIVE FOR ABOUT AN HOUR. COULDN'T FIND MY *CENTER*.

SPORTS

WHA--*IBN*--? HOW DID YOU--? WHERE DID YOU--?

I NEED A NEW *PLACE*.

I TRIED ALL THE *EXERCISES*. THE LAKE, THE MOUNTAIN PEAK...

...THE *TREEHOUSE*...

BLAST IT, IBN, THIS WAS A *NEW SUIT*...

I DOUBT IT'S THE *IMAGERY* AT FAULT HERE...

...BUT, RATHER, MY INABILITY TO MOVE MYSELF *LATERALLY*...GET BEYOND THE *NOW*...

...SINCE THERE WILL *BE* NOTHING AFTER THE *"NOW."*

IBN, THIS IS THE *PENTA-GON*. YOU CAN'T BE HERE. I'M A ONE-CLIENT SHRINK NOW...

TWO. YOU *KNOW* HOW IMPORTANT OUR *WORK* IS.

YOU'RE THE *ONLY* ONE I'VE MADE *ANY* PROGRESS WITH.

YOU ARE MY LIFE LINE, DR. GIBSON. THE *THIN* LINE BETWEEN ME...

...AND *HIM*.

I NEED TO *RETRACE* MY STEPS...

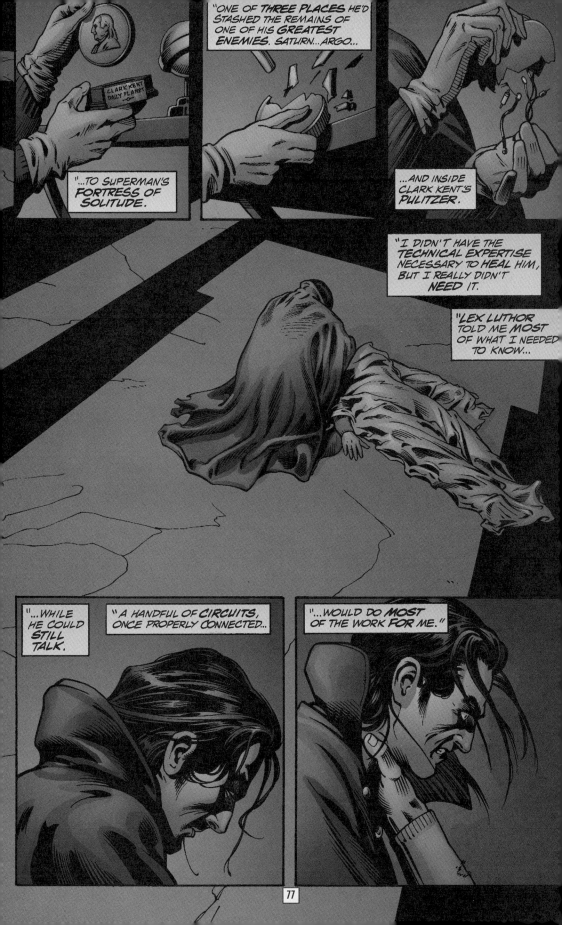

"ONE OF *THREE PLACES* HE'D STASHED THE REMAINS OF ONE OF HIS *GREATEST ENEMIES.* SATURN...ARGO...

"...TO SUPERMAN'S *FORTRESS OF SOLITUDE.*

...AND INSIDE CLARK KENT'S *PULITZER.*

"I DIDN'T HAVE THE *TECHNICAL EXPERTISE* NECESSARY TO HEAL HIM, BUT I REALLY DIDN'T *NEED* IT.

"*LEX LUTHOR* TOLD ME MOST OF WHAT I NEEDED TO KNOW...

"...WHILE HE COULD *STILL TALK.*

"A HANDFUL OF *CIRCUITS,* ONCE PROPERLY *CONNECTED...*

"...WOULD DO *MOST* OF THE WORK *FOR ME.*"

CLARK KENT DAILY PLANET

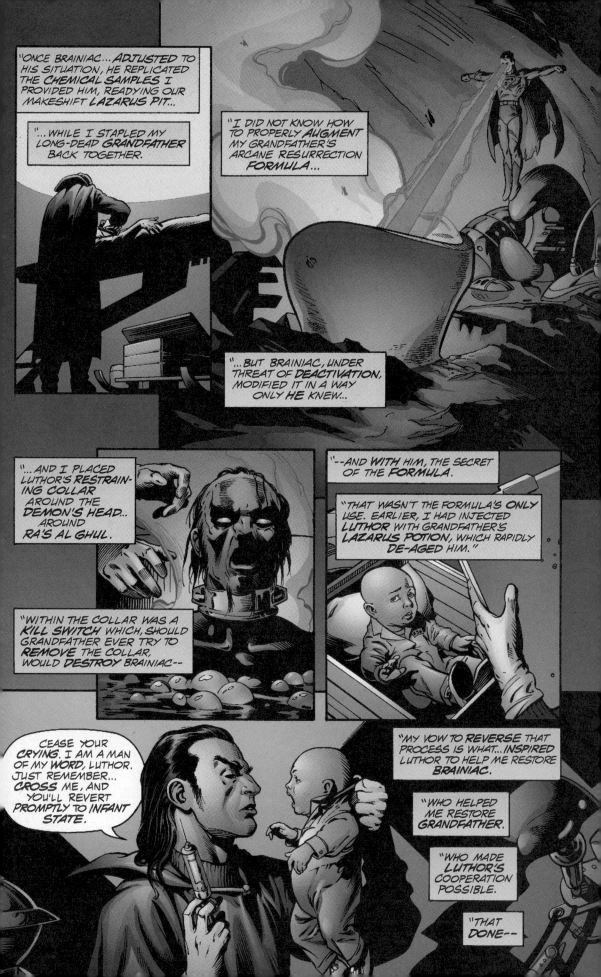

"ONCE BRAINIAC...*ADJUSTED* TO HIS SITUATION, HE REPLICATED THE *CHEMICAL SAMPLES* I PROVIDED HIM, READYING OUR MAKESHIFT *LAZARUS PIT*...

"...WHILE I STAPLED MY *LONG-DEAD GRANDFATHER* BACK TOGETHER.

"I DID NOT KNOW HOW TO PROPERLY *AUGMENT* MY GRANDFATHER'S *ARCANE RESURRECTION FORMULA*...

"...BUT BRAINIAC, UNDER THREAT OF *DEACTIVATION*, MODIFIED IT IN A WAY ONLY *HE* KNEW...

"...AND I PLACED *LUTHOR'S RESTRAINING COLLAR* AROUND THE *DEMON'S HEAD*... AROUND *RA'S AL GHUL*.

"--AND *WITH HIM*, THE SECRET OF THE *FORMULA*.

"THAT WASN'T THE FORMULA'S *ONLY USE*. EARLIER, I HAD INJECTED *LUTHOR* WITH GRANDFATHER'S *LAZARUS POTION*, WHICH RAPIDLY *DE-AGED HIM*."

"WITHIN THE COLLAR WAS A *KILL SWITCH* WHICH, SHOULD GRANDFATHER EVER TRY TO *REMOVE* THE COLLAR, WOULD *DESTROY BRAINIAC*--

CEASE YOUR *CRYING*. I AM A MAN OF MY *WORD*, LUTHOR. JUST REMEMBER... *CROSS ME*, AND YOU'LL REVERT PROMPTLY TO *INFANT STATE*.

"MY VOW TO *REVERSE* THAT PROCESS IS WHAT...*INSPIRED* LUTHOR TO HELP ME RESTORE *BRAINIAC*.

"WHO HELPED ME RESTORE *GRANDFATHER*.

"WHO MADE *LUTHOR'S COOPERATION* POSSIBLE.

"THAT DONE--

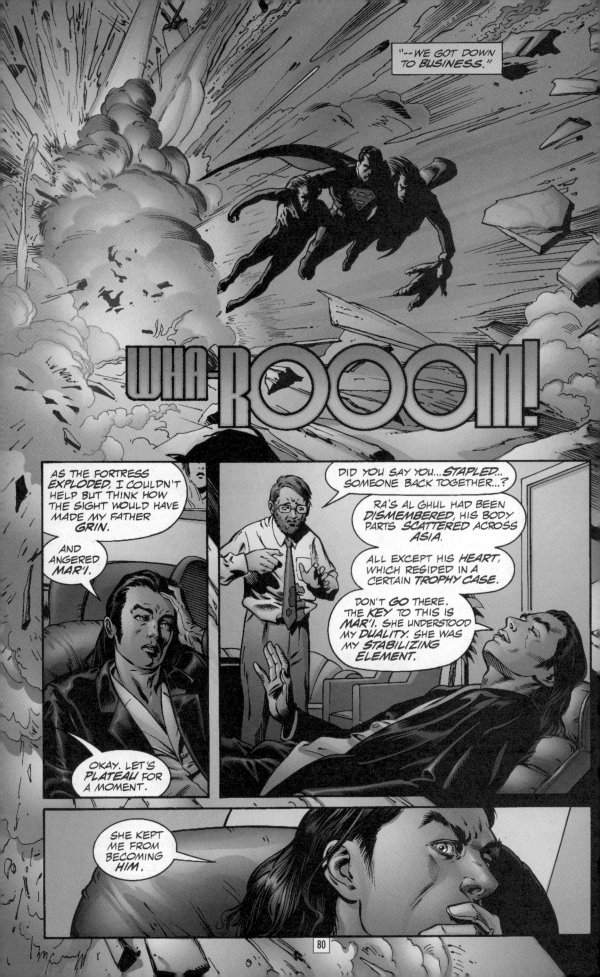

"--WE GOT DOWN TO BUSINESS."

WHA-ROOOOM!

AS THE FORTRESS *EXPLODED*, I COULDN'T HELP BUT THINK HOW THE SIGHT WOULD HAVE MADE MY FATHER *GRIN*.

AND ANGERED *MAR'I*.

OKAY. LET'S *PLATEAU* FOR A MOMENT.

DID YOU SAY YOU... *STAPLED*... SOMEONE BACK TOGETHER...?

RA'S AL GHUL HAD BEEN *DISMEMBERED*, HIS BODY PARTS *SCATTERED* ACROSS ASIA.

ALL EXCEPT HIS *HEART*, WHICH RESIDED IN A CERTAIN *TROPHY CASE*.

DON'T *GO* THERE. THE *KEY* TO THIS IS *MAR'I*. SHE UNDERSTOOD MY *DUALITY*. SHE WAS MY *STABILIZING ELEMENT*.

SHE KEPT ME FROM BECOMING *HIM*.

"I TOOK THEM TO THE TREEHOUSE. I'VE TOLD YOU ABOUT THE TREEHOUSE-- THE SPECIAL PLACE MAR'I AND I SHARED. THE HIDEAWAY BETWEEN EARTH AND TAMARAN BUILT FOR HER WHEN SHE WAS A CHILD."

THE GOOD NEWS, GENTLEMEN, IS THAT YOU'RE ALL ALIVE ONCE MORE.

THE BAD NEWS IS...

...YOU NOW BELONG TO ME...

...AND YOUR RENEWED EXISTENCE WILL BE CUT SHORT AT THE SLIGHTEST DISOBEDIENCE.

AS I HAVE EXPLAINED TO YOU, OUR WORLD IS ENDING. SUPERMAN, BATMAN, AND WONDER WOMAN HAVE FOUND IT NECESSARY TO ALTER OUR TIMESTREAM--

--WITH ACTIONS THAT WILL ALMOST CERTAINLY ERADICATE IT.

"OUR" WORLD--OR YOUR WORLD, HUMAN?

WHO THE DEVIL ARE YOU TO TALK TO ME THIS WAY, YOU WHELP?

A YEAR AGO, YOU WERE JUST ANOTHER FACE AT THE TABLE--! RA'S, SHUT YOUR GRAND-PUP UP!

WERE IT THAT SIMPLE, LUTHOR--

--BUT IBN AL XU'FFASCH HAS WATCHED AND WAITED.

HE KNOWS GOOD AND EVIL ARE BUT--

"--SHIPS ADRIFT IN A STRONG TIDE--

THE ARABIC LANGUAGE LENDS ITSELF QUITE WELL TO POETRY.

--AND HE IS ALSO HIS FATHER'S SON.

VERY WELL. I PRESUME THEN, THAT YOU INTEND TO HAVE US POOL OUR COLLECTIVE GENIUS TO SAVE THIS REALITY.

CORRECT.

I GIVE YOU ONE HOUR.

GO...GO BACK. THE *WORLD* IS... *ENDING*...?

WHICH IS WHY I HAD NO *CHOICE* BUT TO *ALLY* MYSELF WITH THREE SUCH AS *THEY.* YOU SEEM *DISTURBED* BY THAT.

DISTURBED IS... A WORD...

THE END JUSTIFIES THE MEANS.

NIETZSCHE?

AL GHUL...

THOKK THOKK THOKK

THOKK

THOKK THOKK THOKK THOKK THOKK

AAAAAHHHH!

AAAAAAHHH--::

‹SILENCE.›

‹RUH-RELEASE ME, GRANDFATHER--PLEASE--!›

‹I'M SORRY I BROKE MY VOW OF SILENCE--! GIVE ME ANOTHER CHANCE--! I-›

‹YOU ARE THE PRODUCT OF A MOST PERFECT UNION. YOUR FATHER WAS THE WESTERN WORLD'S DARK KNIGHT... YOUR MOTHER, MY DAUGHTER AND FINEST SOLDIER.›

‹AS THEIR ONLY SON, YOU ARE THE HEIR TO MY VAST EMPIRE, BUT THAT IS A BEQUEATHMENT I SWEAR I SHALL NEVER ALLOW YOU...›

‹...UNTIL SUCH TIME AS YOUR COURAGE MEASURES ONE-TENTH OF THEIRS.›

‹BURY HIS FEAR.›

‹NO! PLEASE!›

‹...PLEASE...›

...ENDS AND MEANS...?

WHAT..?

OH, I LED MY UNHOLY TRIO TO THE GREATEST INFORMATION NEXUS IN THE HEMISPHERE...

"...JUST NORTH OF... AND UNDER... GOTHAM CITY."

SIXTY MINUTES, EH? YOUR GENEROSITY IS UNDERWHELMING.

AND JUST HOW ARE WE SUPPOSED TO GO ABOUT PUTTING ARMAGEDDON ON HOLD?

I HAVE NO IDEA. BUT I DO KNOW THIS: YOU THREE ARE ARGUABLY THE MOST BRILLIANT AND RESOURCEFUL MINDS IN HUMAN HISTORY.

IF YOU CAN'T DO THIS...

...IT CAN'T BE DONE.

AGAIN, I GIVE YOU ONE HOUR...PROVIDED WE DO NOT ALL WINK OUT OF EXISTENCE BEFORE THEN.

I CANNOT IMAGINE YOU WOULD NEED ANYTHING BRAINIAC'S NEW BODY COULD NOT PROCURE, BUT IF YOU DO... I'LL BE UPSTAIRS.

"AND THERE I LEFT THEM, HARD AT WORK, EACH IN HIS OWN FASHION."

"AND YOU, IBN?"

I WRESTLED WITH MY OWN DEMONS.

...TO HONOR, AS SHAKESPEARE MIGHT PUT IT, THIS "LITTLE DEATH" YOU HAVE JUST DIED, MY LOVE...

¿HA HA HA HA!?

NO! WAIT! DON'T--

I MEAN IT, IBN! LET ME UP!

IT WAS JUST A JOKE, MAR'I. IN ELIZABETHAN ENGLISH, AS IN FRENCH, "TO DIE" IS ANOTHER WAY OF SAYING--

I KNOW WHAT IT MEANS. I JUST DON'T LIKE TALKING ABOUT DEATH. AND NEVER COVER ME UP LIKE THAT.

IT MAKES ME FEEL LIKE I'M BEING BURIED ALIVE OR SOMETHING.

MAR'I, I'D NEVER--

OH, I KNOW, I *KNOW*. I'M *SORRY*. THAT *STORY*... WHAT YOUR GRANDFATHER *DID* TO YOU... I COULD *KILL* HIM, IBN, IF HE WEREN'T ALREADY--

--I'M *SORRY*, I'M SO SORRY, DARLING. IT'S MY *TEMPER*. IT--

--*PULLS* AT YOU, SOAKING THE SHORE OF YOUR *REASON* LIKE FLOODING *TIDEWATER*...

I *UNDERSTAND*.

YES. YES, YOU *DO*. LIKE NO ONE EVER HAS *BEFORE*.

AND JUST AS I WILL SOMEDAY LEARN TO WED MY *TAMARANIAN IMPULSES* TO MY *EARTHBORN INSTINCTS*...

...*YOU* WILL LEARN TO WALK WITH HEAD HELD *HIGH* THE PATH BETWEEN YOUR FATHER'S ALL-CONSUMING *HEROISM* AND YOUR GRANDFATHER'S *PERVERTED GENIUS*.

"WED." AN INTERESTING CHOICE OF *WORDS*, MY MOST BEAUTIFUL...

"I HATE TO INTERRUPT--

--BUT YOU *DO* REALIZE THOSE TWO ARE GOING TO *DOUBLE-CROSS* YOU?

THEY'RE VILLAINS, FOR PETE'S SAKE.

AND WHY AREN'T YOU *WITH* THEM?

I DESPISE WORKING IN GROUPS. EVERYBODY'S GOT AN *OPINION*.

REST ASSURED, YOUNG MAN, I AM ON *YOUR* SIDE. DON'T WORRY ABOUT THE *OTHERS*.

TRUST ME.

‹GRANDFATHER, *PLEASE...*!›

AND NONE OF THEM COULD SEE WHAT YOU WERE *ACTUALLY* DOING?

TOOK EVERYTHING I *HAD* NOT TO *KILL* HIM.

STILL HAVE ISSUES WITH *FATHER FIGURES.* EVER SINCE...

NEITHER BRAINIAC'S NOR LUTHOR'S *EGO* ALLOWED FOR THE POSSIBILITY THAT I MIGHT BE *SMARTER* THAN THEM.

BUT RA'S SAW IT COMING. HE WAS ALWAYS ONE STEP AHEAD OF ME.

"ALMOST ALWAYS."

NO, LUTHOR AND BRAINIAC DIDN'T KNOW WHAT I *REALLY* WANTED.

BUT THE *DEMON* KNEW.

AH! *THERE'S* THE BOY!

FOR YOUR *PERUSAL,* YOUR EMINENCE--A STORY OF *SUCCESS* SPUN IN *STEEL* AND *CIRCUITRY!* BEHOLD-- THE *CHRONOSLIP!*

ONCE INSIDE ITS *TACHYON FIELD,* WE WILL BE *IMMUNE* TO ANY AND ALL *EFFECTS* OF *CHRONAL TAMPERING--*

--WHISKED SAFELY INTO A *NULLSTREAM* FROM WHICH WE CAN *REENTER* REALITY NO MATTER HOW IT MAY BE *ALTERED.*

SEE FOR *YOURSELF.* AFTER YOU.

NO...

...AFTER *YOU.*

SKKZTTZ

WHAT--?

A *FAIL-SAFE,* BRAINIAC. A *REMOTE CONTROL* I PLANTED INTO YOUR ROBOT BODY JUST BEFORE YOUR *CONSCIOUS- NESS* TOOK HOLD.

MARCH.

NO!

IBN, STOP! I TOLD YOU YOU COULD TRUST ME! YOU--YOU DON'T UNDER-STAND! HE FORCED ME TO--

I UNDERSTAND PERFECTLY. THE TWO OF YOU DOUBLE-CROSSED ME.

IF THIS MACHINE DID WHAT YOU SAID IT WOULD DO, YOU WOULD HAVE ALREADY USED IT AND ABANDONED ME.

OF COURSE, I SUPPOSE THERE IS THE CHANCE YOU COULD BE TELLING THE TRUTH.

LET'S FIND OUT.

FZAAAAK!

"I FELT NO SENSE OF VICTORY. I'D GAMBLED AND LOST. OH, I KNEW THEY'D BETRAY ME... BUT I'D HOPED THAT THEIR SCHEMES WOULD HAVE SUGGESTED A FEASIBLE PLAN.

"APPARENTLY, THEIR SURVIVAL INSTINCT WAS DWARFED BY THE GRAVITATIONAL PULL OF OLD HABITS.

"I WAS NO FURTHER ALONG THAN WHEN I'D STARTED. I STILL HAD NO WORKABLE STRATEGY...

"...AND ONLY ONE LOOSE END."

CIVIL WAR

KTANG!

I **WONDERED** WHAT HAD **BECOME** OF YOU.

I HAD TO **DISTANCE** MYSELF FROM **THEM.** THEY HAD NO **HOPE** OF OUTWITTING YOU.

NEITHER KNOWS HOW TO THINK LIKE A MAN TORN **BETWEEN** GOOD AND EVIL. BRAINIAC, IN PARTICULAR, WAS **BAFFLED** BY YOUR CHAOTIC MIND.

YOU, ON THE OTHER HAND--

I KNOW YOU BETTER THAN YOU KNOW **YOURSELF,** IBN.

ONLY A **VERY AMBITIOUS** MAN WOULD HAVE THE **CONFIDENCE** TO BRING TOGETHER LUTHOR, BRAINIAC, AND RA'S AL GHUL. YOUR **TROUBLE** IS, **DESPITE** THAT AMBITION--

--YOU DON'T KNOW WHAT YOU **WANT.**

I'LL **HUMOR** YOU, OLD MAN. WHAT **DO** I WANT?

ISN'T IT **OBVIOUS?**

YOU WANT TO BE **THE BATMAN.**

WHAT--?

I NAMED YOU *TOO APPROPRIATELY.* "IBN AL XU'FFASCH." ARABIC FOR "SON OF THE *BAT.*"

THERE IS MUCH OF ME *IN* YOU...YET MUCH OF THE *DETECTIVE,* AS WELL. YOUR INSTINCTS...YOUR *METHODS...ARE PURELY HIS.*

THAT'S NOT--

OF ALL THE PLACES ON EARTH YOU COULD HAVE *BROUGHT* US, IBN... WHY THE *BATCAVE?* WHY NOT LEAVE US IN THE EQUALLY WELL-EQUIPPED *FORTRESS...OR ANYWHERE* ELSE?

FACE THE *TRUTH,* IBN. YOU *WANT* TO USURP YOUR FATHER. *EVERY* SON DOES. IN *FACT...*

...THAT WAS ALWAYS MY *PLAN* FOR YOU.

I AM MY *OWN MAN,* GRANDFATHER!

THEN FOLLOW YOUR *OWN* CONVICTIONS.

WHAT'S *BOTHERING* YOU IS *NOT* THAT THE WORLD IS COMING TO AN *END...*

...BUT, RATHER, THAT YOU STOOD BY AND ALLOWED YOUR *BROKEN, AGING, TIRED...MORTAL...FATHER...*

...HIS VERY *BODY* HELD TOGETHER PREDOMINANTLY BY *WILL POWER* ALONE...

...TO ATTEMPT TO *SOLVE* THIS CRISIS IN *YOUR* STEAD.

ONE *COMMON PHILOSOPHY,* MORE THAN *ANYTHING,* UNITES YOU AND YOUR FATHER, IBN.

IF YOU *WANT* SOMETHING DONE *RIGHT...*

≤HKKK≥

...*YOU* HAVE... TO DO IT... *YOURSELF.*

CON...CONGRATULATIONS. YOU HAVE ACCOMPLISHED... THE FIRST OF *MANY* THINGS...THE DETECTIVE *FAILED...* TO DO.

WHAT...

...WHAT AM I SUPPOSED TO *GET* OUT OF ALL THAT...?

TWO THINGS.

FIRST, THAT IN A BREAKTHROUGH *BEYOND* WHAT YOU AND I HAVE EVER KNOWN, MY GRAND-FATHER GAVE ME THE ANSWER TO A QUESTION I DIDN'T KNOW I *HAD*...

...BUT ONE THAT WILL AFFECT THE COURSE OF MY LIFE, HOWEVER SHORT IT MAY BE.

SECOND, IF YOU HAVE LOVED ONES, DOCTOR, I *IMPLORE* YOU...

...MAKE A BETTER PEACE WITH THEM THAN *I* HAVE.

HI, SON. IT'S *DAD.*

YEAH, IT'S BEEN AWHILE. I JUST...

...I JUST THOUGHT WE SHOULD *TALK*...

Matt Haley/Tom Simmons

MEMORANDUM
From: ALAN SCOTT
To: CLARK KENT

Clark:
Success! My power-lantern-created space station -- no longer required for Justice League meetings -- has at last been fully transformed as per your specifications into a complex dubbed "The Green."

IATERIALS ALLO
is ban is *Strictly En*

SO I SAYS, "MAN, I'LL PULL A SIX-MONTH TOUR ON THE GREEN IF IT MEANS I GET T'BE WITHIN A HUNDRED MILES OF THAT NIGHTSTAR CHICK," Y'KNOW?

MOOK. GREEN'S SO BIG, YOU'RE NOT GONNA SEE HER OR HARDLY ANY OF THE SECURITY PATROL, Y'DUMB--

YOU GOT THAT RIGHT! HE WON'T-- NOT ONCE WE TURN HIM RIGHT BACK AROUND FOR IMPORTING CONTRABAND!

WHAT THE HELL'S THE MATTER WITH YOU, NEWBIE? YOU TRYING TO GET US ALL KILLED? CAN'T YOU READ?

HUH?

THAT'S HIM.

DON'T GIVE ME "HUH?"! YOU WERE BRIEFED! THIS STATION WAS CREATED BY GREEN LANTERN! POWERFUL AS HE IS--

Racing the threat of world hunger predicated by the destruction of Kansas, and with the help of thousands of shuttling workers...

...we have managed to create here dozens of *new* farmlands *above* the earth's surface.

Corn and grains are lush and thriving...

...while livestock breeds in numbers great enough to feed entire countries. In fact, given the sole limitation of my emerald energy, there is only one thing the station cannot provide:

Anything that grows on *trees.*

ATTENTION
ABSOLUTELY NO WOODEN
MATERIALS ALLOWED!
...n is Strictly Enforced!

--HIS ENERGY-CON-STRUCTS ARE VULNERABLE TO *WOOD!* SOMETHING AS SMALL AS A *TOOTHPICK*--

--COULD RIP RIGHT THROUGH THE *OUTER WALLS!*

I--I--

--WELL--HOW DUMB *IS* IT T'HAVE PEOPLE SOMEWHERE YA GOTTA BE AFRAIDA *PENCILS,* ANYWAY?

NOT AT *ALL*-- IF WE TOLERATE ZERO RISK. WE SCREEN ALL INCOMING CARGO. END OF *PROBLEM.*

NOTHING *ELSE* CAN *DISRUPT* THE *GREEN.* AFTER ALL...

...HOW MUCH *WOOD* IS THERE IN *SPACE?*

THE KINGDOM

THEY'LL KILL US AAUUGGHH! ROBIN?

IT'S *TRUE!* YOU *KNOW* IT! SUPERMAN, BATMAN, AND WONDER WOMAN HAVE GONE INTO THE *PAST* TO SCREW WITH *TIME!*

ANY *MINUTE* NOW, THEY'LL CHANGE HISTORY-- WIPE US ALL FROM EXISTENCE!

THATABOY, MANOTAUR. START A *PUBLIC PANIC.* THAT'LL HELP.

I TRACKED YOU HERE TO KEEP YOU FROM DOING *JUST THAT.* WANNA *PLAY ALONG?*

DAD? WHAT THE HELL ARE *YOU* DOING HERE?

MOVE AWAY FROM THE *THREAT!* THAT IS AN *ORDER!*

WE'RE FACING *CERTAIN DEATH!* HOW CAN YOU *JOKE?*

LISTEN TO *YOU.* MY LITTLE BUDDING *BOTANIST* GETS A SUMMER JOB WORKING *GREEN SECURITY* AND SUDDENLY SHE'S *ORION.*

YOUR *GRANDFATHER* WOULD BE *PROUD.*

LIFETIME OF *PRACTICE.* RANDALL, I'VE KNOWN YOU SINCE YOU AND MAR'I WERE *KNEE-HIGH.* YOU'RE A *GOOD KID,* AND THIS IS A *BAD TIME.*

WHY DON'T YOU GO HOME TO YOUR *LOVED ONES,* SON, AND PREPARE FOR THE *WORST?*

THERE YOU ARE!

FOUND HER, KORY! SHE'S IN THE TREEHOUSE!

MAR'I, SWEETIE, MOMMY AND I HAVE BEEN LOOKING ALL *OVER* FOR YOU! IS EVERYTHING ALL *RIGHT*?

S'FINE.

ISN'T IT *BEAUTIFUL* OUT HERE, MAR'I? WHEN YOUR *MOMMY'S* FROM *ANOTHER PLANET,* A *TREEHOUSE* BECOMES SOMETHING SPECIAL INDEED!

A LITTLE POCKET OF *TAMARANIAN* ATMOSPHERE INSIDE AN ITTY-BITTY *TRANS-WARP SINGULARITY.* UNCLE VIC ALWAYS DOES GIVE MAR'I THE BEST *BIRTHDAY* PRESENTS.

HE'S NOT MY UNCLE.

HE'S A *FRIEND,* THOUGH. WHAT'S *WRONG,* STARSHINE?

MATT? AT *SCHOOL?* HIS *GRAMMA* CAME TO TELL US STORIES?

SOUNDS NEAT.

I DON'T HAVE A GRAMMA.

RANDY, KNOCK IT OFF! DAD'S RIGHT! YOU'RE NOT HELPING ANYTHING!

WHY ARE YOU SIDING WITH HIM? DIDN'T YOU HEAR ME? WE'RE DEAD ALREADY! WE'RE NOT EVEN HERE!

YOU--HIM-- ME--ALL OF THESE PEOPLE ON THE STATION--

I'M GOING TO DO US ALL A FAVOR BY GETTING A JUMP ON DESTRUCTION!

AAAAAAAH!

I KNOW ABOUT THE STATION MAP, MAR'I--AND HOW VULNERABLE IT IS--

--TO THE RIGHT WEAPON--!

--CAN SEE THE *VEGA* STAR OVER *THERE,* AVIA. *LOOK.*

SINCE MOM AND DAD *SPLIT UP,* I VISIT HER AND UNCLE *R'YANDER* ON THE *TAMARANIAN OUTPOST* THERE EVERY *SUMMER.*

IT'S SUCH A *DIFFERENT* WORLD. I MEAN...THEIR HISTORY IS FRAUGHT WITH *WAR,* BUT EVEN SO, YOU RARELY HEAR STORIES ABOUT *RANDOM* DEATHS.

YOU *MISS* HER, DON'T YOU?

I *MISS* HAVING HER TALK *SENSE* TO *DAD.* CAN YOU *BELIEVE* HE'S *BACK* IN *ACTION* AT *HIS* AGE?

AS "ROBIN" YET. TELL ME *THAT'S* NOT A...WHAT DO THEY CALL IT? MID-LIFE *CRISIS.*

SO? YOUR DAD'S *ALWAYS* BEEN A HERO, RIGHT? EVER SINCE HE WAS A *KID?*

YEAH, I *KNOW,* RANDY, BUT...BUT HE'S ONLY *HUMAN.* AND I MEAN *EARTH*-HUMAN. YOU KNOW...

...*VULNERABLE?* MAR'I, YOU DWELL ON MATTERS OF LOSS *FAR* TOO *MUCH.* DO YOU *EVER* THINK ABOUT ANYTHING *ELSE?*

OH, EVERY *NOW* AND THEN. FOR INSTANCE, I'VE BEEN THINKING A LOT ABOUT THAT *GUY* WE SAW WITH OLLIE *QUEEN.*

THE *TALL, DARK* ONE WITH THE *CLOAK...?*

IBN AL XU'FFASCH? I KNOW!

AGAIN WITH THE *CLOAK* GUY...

HE'S *DANGEROUS...* BUT, DEAR *HIGHFATHER,* YOU COULD *LOSE* YOURSELF IN THOSE EYES FOR...FOR...

FOR AN *ETERNITY.*

FRANKLY, MAR'I, I'M SURPRISED YOU'RE EVEN *HERE*. I WOULD'VE THOUGHT, UNDER THE *CIRCUMSTANCES*, YOU'D BE WITH IBN.

WHAT? AND RISK YOUR DIS-APPROVAL?

MAR'I, DON'T BE THAT WAY. WHATEVER'S EATING AT YOU, TELL ME--WHILE YOU STILL--

AOOGAH AOOGAH

AOOGAH AOOGAH

NO! WE'RE TOO LATE! RANDY'S CARVED HIS WAY INTO THE VAULT!

MANOTAUR... RANDY...YOU'VE GOT TO CALM DOWN!

FOR WHAT IT'S WORTH, I AGREE WITH YOU! I REALLY DO!

WE CAN'T JUST SIT HERE WHILE EVERYTHING WE KNOW CEASES TO EXIST!

WELCOME TO THE PARTY! NOW, LET ME AT THE MAP!

CAN'T DO IT, RANDY. NOT GONNA LET YOU KILL THESE PEOPLE.

IT'S A BAD IDEA.

YOU'VE HAD WORSE.

--CAN CERTAINLY COUNT ON THE SUPER-HEROES TO DO WHATEVER WE *CAN* TO HELP *REBUILD* IN THE WAKE OF THE *KANSAS DISASTER,* MR. SECRETARY--

NOT TO *INTERRUPT,* DICK...BUT HAVE YOU NOTICED WHO YOUR DAUGHTER'S *DANCING* WITH?

HIS NAME IS *IBN AL XU'FFASCH.* POTENTIAL HEIR TO *RA'S AL GHUL'S* EMPIRE.

HOW DO YOU LIKE *THAT?*

I *DON'T.* BUT MAR'I'S *RESPONSIBLE* ENOUGH TO MAKE HER *OWN* CHOICES.

NO DOUBT. VERY WELL.

OH...AND BY THE *WAY...* ABOUT HIS *PARENTAGE...*

ABSOLUTELY *NOT*. NO WAY. *NONE*.

SAID THE *CAPULET* TO THE *MONTAGUE*. IT'S HARDLY *INCEST*, DAD. *GRANDPA* NEVER EVEN *KNEW* ABOUT *IBN* UNTIL *RECENTLY*--

"I *FORBID* YOU TO SEE HIM!"

DON'T YOU THINK I'M A LITTLE *OLD* FOR THIS, DAD?

YOU'RE STILL *MY DAUGHTER*, MAR'I--

--WHICH MEANS YOU *CANNOT* DATE *BRUCE WAYNE'S* SON.

--BECAUSE *IBN* WAS BROUGHT UP BY *RA'S AL GHUL* AND THE *LEAGUE OF ASSASSINS!* FORGIVE ME FOR NOT TRUSTING HIS *PEDIGREE!*

YOU *SHOULDN'T BE* HERE.

BUT I *AM*. AND IT IS ONLY FAIR TO *WARN* YOU, I HAVE NO INTENTION OF *LEAVING*.

I SHOULD TRY TO *PERSUADE* YOU TO CHANGE YOUR *MIND*, MISS *GRAYSON*.

IF ANYONE *COULD*, IT WOULD BE *YOU*, IBN, YOU'RE A VERY *PERSUASIVE MAN*, AREN'T YOU?

WITH A FEW *CALM WORDS* ON BEHALF OF MY *GRANDFATHER*, YOU PERSUADE MEMBERS OF THE *MANKIND LIBERATION FRONT* TO DELAY THEIR *GRANDEST PLANS*.

AND WITH THESE *LAZARUS PITS*, YOU PERSUADE *DEATH* TO IGNORE YOUR *IMMORTAL FAMILY*.

AND WITH THOSE *EYES*, YOU PERSUADE ME TO...

I KNOW WHY YOU SHOWED UP HERE, RANDY!

I UNDER-STAND! DO YOU?

CHRAK

YOU WERE LOOKING FOR SOMEONE TO BE WITH! YOU WERE LOOKING FOR FAMILY... AND I'M THE CLOSEST YOU'VE GOT!

BUT I WISH YOU HADN'T, RANDY!

I WISH YOU HADN'T COME.

MAR'I, I'M SCARED TOO. WE ALL ARE.

I CAN'T DEAL WITH FAMILY RIGHT NOW. I'VE BEEN AFRAID ALL MY LIFE OF SAYING GOODBYE TO ALL OF YOU WHEN THE... WHEN THE END...

DON'T YOU SEE? THAT'S WHY I RAN AWAY FROM YOU ALL...

YOU'RE TRYING TO TRICK ME INTO ADMITTING IT? OF COURSE I'M SCARED. AND DO YOU KNOW WHY?

116

HOW DO YOU FEEL, STARSHINE?

... FREE.

DAD, I... I HAVE TO GO.

GO--?

BELIEVE IT OR NOT, RANDY HAD THE RIGHT IDEA. WE DO HAVE TO ACCEPT THE TRUTH... BUT WE DON'T HAVE TO GIVE UP.

IF THERE'S ANYTHING... ANYTHING... THAT CAN BE DONE...

... I PROMISE YOU I'LL FIND IT!

TO BE
CONTINUED

Frank Quitely

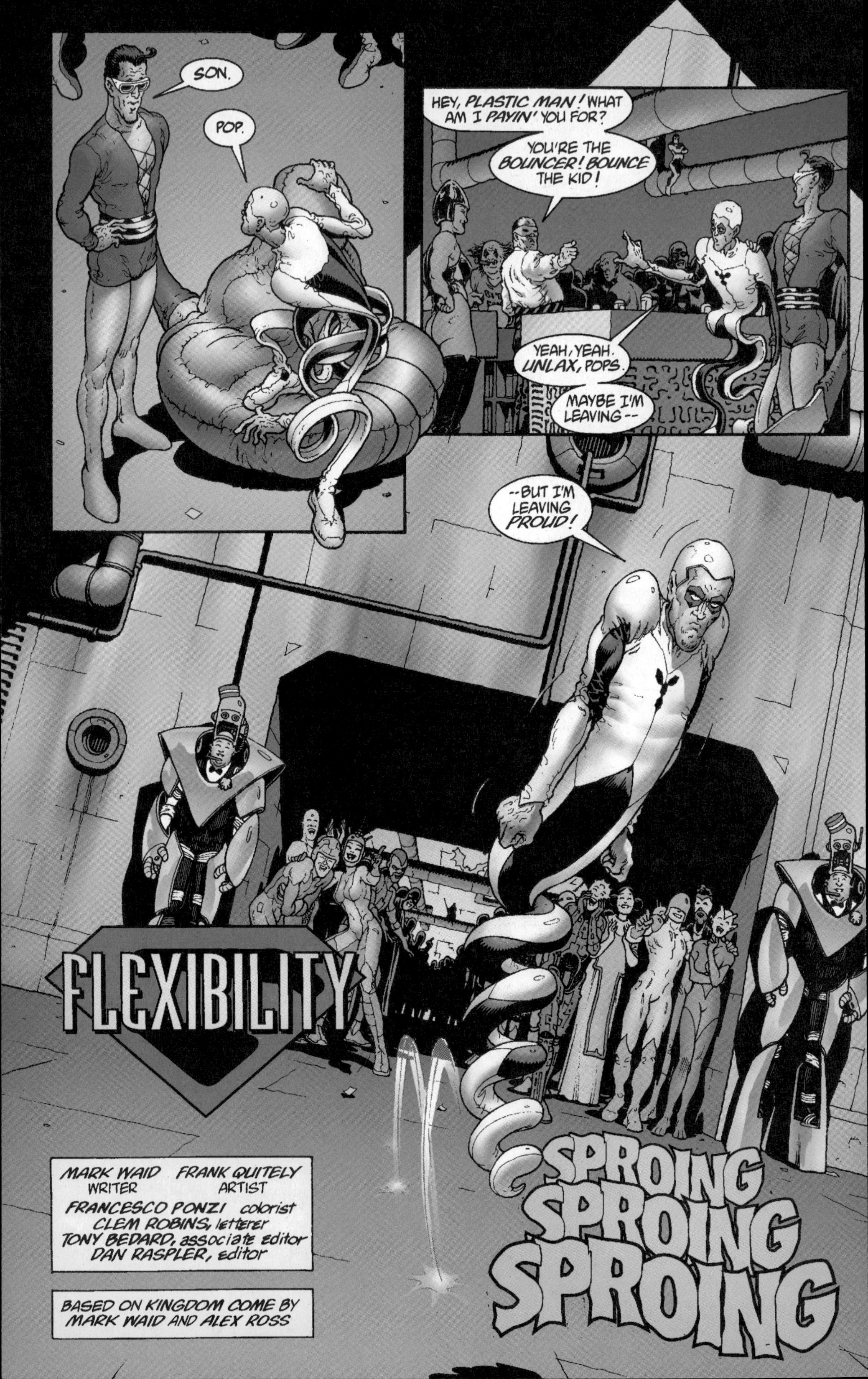

SON.

POP.

HEY, *PLASTIC MAN!* WHAT AM I *PAYIN'* YOU FOR?

YOU'RE THE *BOUNCER!* BOUNCE THE KID!

YEAH, YEAH. UNLAX, POPS.

MAYBE I'M LEAVING --

-- BUT I'M LEAVING *PROUD!*

FLEXIBILITY

SPROING SPROING SPROING

MARK WAID FRANK QUITELY
WRITER   ARTIST

FRANCESCO PONZI colorist
CLEM ROBINS, letterer
TONY BEDARD, associate editor
DAN RASPLER, editor

BASED ON KINGDOM COME BY
MARK WAID AND ALEX ROSS

LOOK! IT'S OFFSPRING!

"THE JIG IS UP." WHO SAYS THAT? WHAT IS WRONG WITH ME? WHAT WAS I--

AAAUGH! "THIS CASE IS WRAPPED UP!" THAT'S WHAT I SHOULDA SAID!

DO SOMETHING FUNNY, OFFSPRING!

THIS CASE IS WRAPPED UP!

"THIS CASE IS WRAPPED UP!" YES! YOU MORON!

MAKE ME LAFF!

SPROING

WHY, THAT'S NOT OFFSPRING! HE'S... BATMAN!

HITCHIN' A RIDE, ARE YOU? AREN'T YOU STILL ON DUTY AT THE RAVE?

GAVE SOLOMON GRUNDY A FIVE TO COVER MY SHIFT. TOLD HIM IT WAS A FIFTY.

SO WHAT'S WITH THE GRIM AND GRITTY APPROACH ALL OF A SUDDEN?

I THOUGHT YOU WERE HAPPY BEING A CLOWN LIKE YOUR OLD MAN.

I'M STRETCHING. POP, THIS WHOLE END-OF-THE-WORLD THING THOSE GUYS WERE GASSING ABOUT... HAVE YOU HEARD ANYTHING ABOUT IT? IS IT TRUE?

LET'S HOPE SO. I OWE A FORTUNE IN TAXES THIS QUARTER. I HAVE GOT TO GET A CUT OF THIS MERCHANDISING...

YOU WANNA COME UP? GOT COLD GINGOLD IN THE FRIDGE.

I'LL ... GET HOME. I'LL TELL YOUR MOM YOU SAID "HI."

ENJOY THE NIGHT. HAVE SOME LAUGHS.

127

RATTLE RATTLE

PWUNT

URK.

THE JIG IS UP, ERNIE.

LOCKED. NO *SURPRISE*. TOLD MICHELINE I'D BE *HOME* BY NOW. SHE'S PROBABLY IN *BED*, FAST *ASLEEP*--

"JUG." "JUG" IS FUNNIER.

YOU'RE *CRITICIZING?*

WHILE YOU CONTROL THE *OXYGEN?* NOPE. BY THE WAY, YOU LOOK LOVELY TONIGHT. DID I *MENTION* THAT?

Hmmm...MY VERY OWN *GENIE* IN A *BOTTLE*. WHATEVER DO I *WISH* FOR...? *HmmHmm*...HOW ABOUT...

...A BOY-FRIEND WHO CAN TELL *TIME?*

I *KNOW* WHAT TIME IT IS. IT'S TIME YOU WERE NICER TO MY *DAD*.

OH. HE *SAW* ME...?

I THINK. WHAT *IS* IT WITH YOU AND HIM, MIKE?

NNNNOTHING. HE'S JUST... ALWAYS *AROUND*, Y'KNOW?

"EVEN WHEN WE WERE *KIDS*, HE WAS ALWAYS...*THERE*. AT YOUR *PARTIES*..."

MORE... CAKE...?

... NO.

ALL RIGHT! WHO'S ON *MY* TEAM? BILLY? LATIEF? LET'S GO, MEN!

GONNA... *CHUNK*...

OH, OKAY...I'LL LEAVE YOU *ALONE* NOW...

"...ON *PROM* NIGHT..."

HEY, BUSTER, WATCH THOSE *HANDS*!

? DAAAAD--!

AHHH, I'LL LEAVE YOU *ALONE* NOW.

BUT FIRST--SAY *CHEESE*!

"...ON *EVERY* NIGHT..."

GOOD ONE.

I THOUGHT SO. I'LL LEAVE YOU *ALONE* NOW.

PROMISES, PROMISES...

129

I PICK UP SCARLET'S TRAIL AND LEAVE MESSAGES WITH THE GANG TO *MEET* ME.

IT'S BEEN AWHILE, BUT I SHOULD BE EASY FOR THEM TO SPOT IF THEY'RE LOOKING.

"...*NEVER SICKER!*"

H-WHORRG-G

I'M THE ONE WHO NEEDS A *SHOWER.*

THERE. FEEL *BETTER?*

YES.

WHY ISHT THE *ALLEYWAY* SHPINNING?

...YEAH, I GOT THE MAP. YOU'RE *DRIVING,* RIGHT?

...OoOOOHH...

HOW MANY TIMES I GOTTA *TELL* YOU? "*LIQUOR,* THEN *BEER,* NEVER *FEAR.*"

"*BEER,* THEN *LIQUOR...*"

STILL, THE EAVESDROPPING'S PAYING *OFF.* I KNOW THEY HAVE A *MAP*--THEY'RE *HEADED* SOME-WHERE--

--AND I CAN FIND OUT *EXACTLY WHERE* IF I CAN ESCAPE THEIR *DETECTION* JUST *ONE MORE MIN*--

HI, ERNIE!

DO YOU *MIND?* I'M ON *STAKEOUT* HERE!

¿HMRFF!?

SORRY, ERN. CHILL. WE'RE HERE TO *HELP,* MY SIDE-KICK AND I!

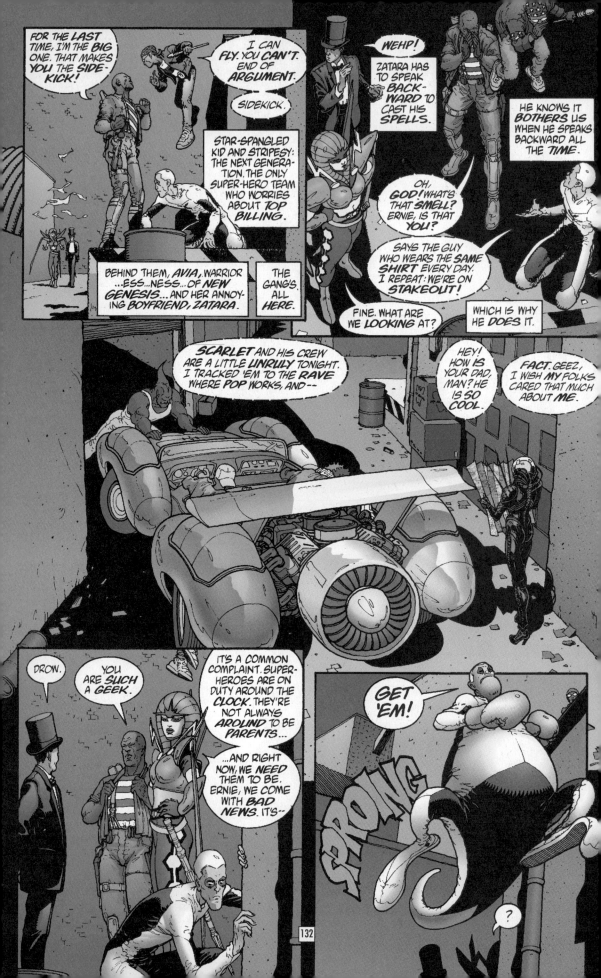

FOR THE *LAST* TIME, I'M THE *BIG* ONE. THAT MAKES *YOU* THE *SIDE-KICK!*

I CAN *FLY.* YOU *CAN'T.* END OF *ARGUMENT.*

SIDEKICK.

STAR-SPANGLED KID AND STRIPESY: THE NEXT GENERA-TION. THE ONLY SUPER-HERO TEAM WHO WORRIES ABOUT *TOP BILLING.*

BEHIND THEM, *AVIA,* WARRIOR ...ESS...NESS... OF *NEW GENESIS...* AND HER ANNOY-ING *BOYFRIEND, ZATARA.*

THE GANG'S ALL HERE.

WEHP!

ZATARA HAS TO SPEAK *BACK-WARD* TO CAST HIS SPELLS.

HE KNOWS IT *BOTHERS* US WHEN HE SPEAKS BACKWARD ALL THE *TIME.*

OH, *GOD!* WHAT'S THAT *SMELL?* ERNIE, IS THAT *YOU?*

SAYS THE GUY WHO WEARS THE *SAME SHIRT* EVERY DAY. I REPEAT: WE'RE ON *STAKEOUT!*

FINE. WHAT ARE WE *LOOKING* AT?

WHICH IS WHY HE *DOES* IT.

SCARLET AND HIS CREW ARE A LITTLE *UNRULY* TONIGHT. I TRACKED 'EM TO THE *RAVE* WHERE POP WORKS, AND --

HEY! HOW IS YOUR DAD, MAN? HE IS SO *COOL.*

FACT. GEEZ. I WISH *MY* FOLKS CARED THAT MUCH ABOUT *ME.*

DROW.

YOU ARE *SUCH* A GEEK.

IT'S A COMMON COMPLAINT. SUPER-HEROES ARE ON DUTY AROUND THE *CLOCK.* THEY'RE NOT ALWAYS *AROUND* TO BE PARENTS...

...AND RIGHT NOW, WE NEED THEM TO BE. ERNIE, WE COME WITH *BAD NEWS.* IT'S--

GET 'EM!

SPRONG

?

THEN IT'S *TRUE.*

WE DON'T KNOW THE *WHYS* OR THE *HOWS,* ERNIE...BUT I HEARD IT RIGHT FROM *NIGHTSTAR.* SUPER-MAN, BATMAN, WONDER WOMAN...I THINK THEY'RE *ALREADY* GONE.

THEN LET'S *GEAR!* NOW WE'VE *GOTTA* GET SCARLET'S GANG! THEY'RE OUT TO STEAL SOME-THING *BIG,* AND THIS IS OUR *LAST CHANCE* TO *STOP* 'EM ONCE AND FOR *ALL!*

TO BE *HEROES!*

SPROING

DEPPIHW.

YOU'VE BEEN TALKING TO *MICHELINE* AGAIN, HAVEN'T YOU?

NO! YES NO!

THIS IS ABOUT WHAT I HAVE TO DO! THIS ISN'T FOR *HER!* IT'S FOR *ME!*

ISN'T IT?

134

IS *THIS* WHAT YOU WANT?

MAYBE A LITTLE LESS *CAPE*... BUT OTHERWISE NOT *BAD*. YOU'RE *HOME* ALREADY?

WE NEED TO TALK, MIKE.

SOUNDS *SERIOUS*.

WHAT *ISN'T* WITH *YOU*?

WHAT'S *THAT* SUPPOSED TO MEAN?

I JUST REALLY GET THE *FEELING* SOMETIMES THAT YOU DON'T *LIKE ME FUNNY*. LIKE THERE'S SOMETHING *WRONG* WITH THE WAY POP BROUGHT ME *UP*.

MIKE, WHY ARE YOU ALWAYS TRYING TO COME *BETWEEN* ME AND HIM?

ERNIE, I'M NOT--

YES. YES, YOU *ARE*. POP *NEVER* FEELS *WELCOME* IN THIS PLACE.

:SIGH: I JUST...

...OKAY, YOU'RE *RIGHT*. HE GETS ON MY *NERVES*. HE'S A *GOOFBALL*, ERNIE!

YOU SAY THAT LIKE IT'S A *BAD* THING.

CAN YOU STOP JOKING FOR EVEN A *SECOND*? THIS IS *SERIOUS*! LOOK AT US, ERNIE, LOOK AT OUR *LIVES*!

WE'RE *NEVER* INVITED TO PARTIES ON CAMPUS... MY FRIENDS DON'T *EVER* COME OVER...

...IT WAS *COOL* IN *HIGH SCHOOL*, BUT WE'RE *COLLEGE AGE* NOW! YOU TWO CAN'T BE *"CLOWN AND SON"* FOREVER!

BOOM

SO MUCH FOR THE SNEAK ATTACK.

I SEE. COULD *YOU* TELEPORT US TO EGYPT? PERHAPS SHOOT US ACROSS THE ATLANTIC IN A *BIG RUBBER SLINGSHOT?* NO?

THEN SHUT UP!

KOOL! EREHT YEHT ERA!

SPRONG

WHAT DID HE SAY? ONE MORE *TIME* WITH THAT *BACKWARDS CRAP* AN' I'MONNA *BELT* HIM--!

HE SAID, "THERE THEY *ARE*"-- *GRAVEROBBING* THE *SPHINX!*

BUT *WHY?*

WHO AM I, THE *RIDDLER?*

JUST HIT THEM BEFORE THEY FIND WHATEVER IT IS THEY'RE--

IS THAT...?

IT'S BRAINIAC'S STARSHIP!

I HAVEN'T SEEN THAT SINCE I WAS A KID!

WOW.

HE MUSTA HIDDEN IT HERE AFTER SUPERMAN WHUPPED HIS—YOU GOT IT! OR, RATHER—

--WE'VE GOT IT--SO NUKE OFF! IT'S OURS!

WE'RE GONNA USE IT TA BLOW THIS MUDBALL--FIND SOME SAFE PLANET, Y'KNOW? MAYBE YOU FEEBS ARE STUCK HERE FOR THE BIG BANG, BUT ME--

--ARMAGEDDON OUTTA HERE!

BUDDA BUDDA BUDDA

FORGET IT, SCARLET! THIS CASE IS WRAPPED UP!

ERNIE, NO! LET THEM... ...LET THEM GO.

GOOD ONE.

I SUPPOSE WE'RE *DONE* HERE. LET'S GO HOME AND...

...AND...

...AND WAIT FOR THE *END*, I GUESS.

PERHAPS MY *FATHER'S* FOUND AN ESCAPE...THOUGH I *DOUBT* IT.

MAYBE...MAYBE WE *ALL* OUGHTTA TRY T'FIND OUR FOLKS, HUH?

TAHW EH DIAS--

WHAK

WWWO!

YOU GUYS GO ON. I'LL CATCH UP.

HOW'D *YOU* GET HERE?

SHOT MYSELF ACROSS THE ATLANTIC IN A BIG RUBBER SLINGSHOT. HEARD ABOUT THE *WHIZ WAGON* THEFT, FOLLOWED THE *TRAIL*.

I THOUGHT... YOU KNOW...MAYBE WE OUGHT TO BE *TOGETHER*. THIS *RAGNAROK* STUFF--

--IT'S *LEGIT*. YOU *HEARD*. YOU *HAVE* BEEN BUSY.

YOU DON'T KNOW THE *HALF* OF IT. I TALKED WITH *MICHELINE*.

KINDA.

AND I... I WANT TO *APOLOGIZE*.

FOR *WHAT?*

SHE PUT IT TO ME *STRAIGHT*, ERNIE. SHE SAID IN YOUR *WHOLE LIFE*, I NEVER GAVE YOU ANYTHING *WORTHWHILE*.

ARE YOU *KIDDING?*

YOU GAVE ME *EVERY-THING.*

I NEVER LEFT YOU *ALONE.*

NO. NO, YOU *DIDN'T.*

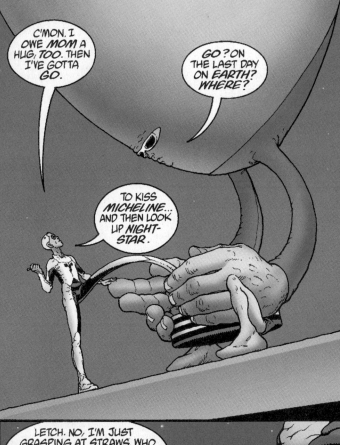

C'MON. I OWE *MOM* A HUG, *TOO*. THEN I'VE GOTTA GO.

GO? ON THE LAST DAY ON *EARTH*? WHERE?

TO KISS *MICHELINE*... AND THEN LOOK UP *NIGHT-STAR*.

NIGHTSTAR?

OKAY. YOU WIN. THAT'S WHAT *I'D* DO, *TOO*.

LETCH. NO, I'M JUST GRASPING AT STRAWS. WHO KNOWS? SHE'S SMART. MAYBE SHE'S FIGURED OUT SOME WAY TO *MOBILIZE* AGAINST ARMAGEDDON.

BEATS WAITING FOR *OBLIVION*.

YOU WANT TO *FIGHT* THIS? *SERIOUSLY*?

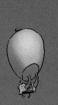

I NEVER SAID "*SERIOUSLY*."

TO BE CONTINUED

Mark Pajarillo/Walden Wong

IT'S IN MY OWN *FAMILY* THAT THE *NIGHTMARE* LIVES ON.

MY NAME IS *IRIS WEST,* AND I'M THE *FASTEST GIRL* ALIVE...

...WHICH ISN'T ANYWHERE NEAR FAST *ENOUGH* TO *CATCH UP* WITH MY *FATHER,* THE *FLASH...*

QUICK FIX

MARK WAID–writer MARK PAJARILLO–pencils WALDEN WONG–inks
KEN LOPEZ–letters ROB SCHWAGER–colors and seps
TONY BEDARD–assistant editor DAN RASPLER–editor

Based on
KINGDOM COME
by MARK WAID and
ALEX ROSS

...AS HE RUNS *AWAY* FROM HIS *FAILURES.*

THE KINGDOM

I GUESS THAT'S THE BIGGEST *PROBLEM* WITH BEING ABLE TO DO THE IMPOSSIBLE.

YOU GET *USED* TO IT. AND THEN *ONE DAY,* THE IMPOSSIBLE IS IMPOSSIBLE EVEN FOR YOU.

MY DAD IS MY *HERO.* BEFORE THE *KANSAS DISASTER,* HE WAS THE GUARDIAN ANGEL OF *KEYSTONE CITY.* HE VOWED HE'D NEVER LET ANYTHING *BAD* HAPPEN THERE.

AND THEN ONE DAY, DESPITE HIS *EFFORTS...*

...THE CITY WAS *GONE.*

I TELL MYSELF THAT'S THE REASON WHY, EVEN THOUGH HE SAYS HE *LOVES* ME, HE *HATES* TO BE *WITH* ME.

I REMIND HIM OF WHAT IT FELT LIKE TO BE A *PROUD MAN.*

IRIS! WAIT!

FOOD BANK

PAT? HAVE YOU SEEN MY *DAD* AROUND?

THE *FLASH?* DOES ANYONE ACTUALLY *SEE* HIM ANYMORE?

GUESS *NOT.* BUT IF YOU *DO*--

--I'LL *TELL* HIM WHAT GOOD *VOLUNTEER WORK* YOU'RE DOING, AND HOW OUR ORGANIZATION COULDN'T SURVIVE *WITHOUT YOU.*

IRIS, I'M **SURE** HE **KNOWS.** I'M **SURE** HE'S VERY PROUD.

I'LL HAVE THESE DELIVERED WITHIN THE NEXT FIVE **MINUTES,** PAT.

THAT MUST HAVE BEEN THE **YOUNG GIRL** YOU WERE **TELLING** ME ABOUT. SHE SEEMS VERY **HELPFUL.**

IF ONLY I COULD HELP **HER** IN **TURN,** NORMAN. SOMETHING WEIGHS **HEAVILY** ON HER...

"...BUT **WHAT?"**

IT ISN'T **TRUE** THAT NOBODY EVER SEES MY **DAD.**

DAD! DAD, OVER HERE!

THE FLASH HAS LIVED IN THE SPEED FORCE FOR ALMOST MY ENTIRE LIFE, PREVENTING CRIMES AND ACCIDENTS AROUND THE CLOCK.

I SEE HIM ALL THE TIME.

HE JUST NEVER SEES ME.

GOOD NIGHT, HONEY. I LOVE YOU.

FOR YEARS, HE'S ONLY COMMUNICATED WITH ME IN HOLOGRAPHIC MESSAGES--MAGNETIZED VIBRATIONS HE LEAVES IN THE ATMOSPHERE.

TALK ABOUT PARENTING ON AUTOMATIC PILOT.

YOU'D THINK OUR PATHS WOULD CROSS MORE OFTEN... BUT EVER SINCE I'VE PUT ON THIS *SUIT*, THERE'S BEEN A *BARRIER* BETWEEN US.

WHY DOESN'T HE *APPROVE* OF ME? WHY WON'T HE CALL ME "*KID FLASH*" EVEN ONCE? AM I DOING SOMETHING *WRONG*?

OR IS IT THAT HE ALWAYS COUNTED ON HIS BOOTS BEING FILLED BY--

OH!

KRAASH

--BARRY.

HEY, SIS!

MMMMMM! THANKS FOR LUNCH!

I HAVE TO GO TO WORK. IF THE WORLD HAS ONE DAY LEFT, I'M GOING TO MAKE IT A *PERFECT* ONE. NO CRIMES, NO ACCIDENTS.

IT'S A BIG JOB. I INVITE YOU TO HELP, SON, OR AT THE VERY LEAST--

--STAY OUT OF MY WAY.

GOOD NIGHT. I LOVE YOU.

THIS... THIS IS FOR *REAL?*

DOESN'T COME ANY MORE REAL THAN *THIS,* HUMMING-BIRD.

AND YOU'RE...NOT *SCARED* OF IT?

I ALWAYS *WAS* A FATALIST.

SINCE MOM DIED.

THERE'S A *BUZZ* OUT THAT *NIGHTSTAR'S* LOOKING TO PUT SOME GUYS TOGETHER TO *HELP* SOMEHOW, BUT I'M NOT THE VOLUNTEERING *TYPE,* SO...

...LOOK, THE WAY I SEE IT, WE'VE GOT ONE MORE DAY TO GLORIOUSLY *WASTE.* DO IT *TOGETHER?*

BARRY WEST! IS THIS SOME KIND OF *PRANK...?*

ASK ME TOMORROW.

IT WASN'T ALWAYS *LIKE* THIS.

IT SEEMS TO ME THAT WE WERE HAPPY ONCE...

...WEREN'T WE?

--IS HOW YOU CAN NOT *UNDERSTAND* THE *IMPORTANCE* OF THE *LEGACY* WE CARRY! MY *UNCLE* WAS FLASH BEFORE *ME*--THERE WAS A FLASH BEFORE *HIM*--

GOD, IF YOUR *MOTHER* COULD HEAR YOU! YOU WERE *BORN* WITH A *RESPONSIBILITY*--

WHAT DO YOU WANT ME TO *DO,* DAD? STAND OUT IN A *LIGHTNING STORM* WITH A GIANT *FORK* AND A CASE-LOAD OF *CHEMICALS?*

DON'T GET SMART WITH *ME!* YOU WERE *BORN* WITH *SPEED POWERS*--

--BUT YOU'RE NOT *ABOUT* TO EARN THE MANTLE OF THE *FLASH* ON THAT *COUCH!*

BOO-HOO. 'CAUSE AS FAR AS THIS *COUCH* GOES, CONSIDER ME *PARKED.*

CONSIDER YOURSELF IN A *HELL* OF A LOT OF *TROUBLE*, YOUNG MAN, UNLESS YOU--

I'LL DO IT!

I'LL BE KID FLASH!

I'M AS

FAST AS

IRIS...

...STOP.

THIS IS SERIOUS.

HIM, DAD!

LOOK AT ME!

LOOK AT ME!

THIS ISN'T *OVER*, BARRY.

HAVEN'T, LIKE, FIFTEEN PEOPLE *DIED* WHILE YOU'VE BEEN STANDING HERE *GUILTING* ME?

WHEN I MADE A MORE *OFFICIAL* *DEBUT* LATER, IT WAS MET WITH THE *SAME DISINTEREST.*

I THOUGHT DAD WOULD COME TO *APPROVE,* IN *TIME...*

...BUT I GUESS THERE ISN'T ANY MORE TIME.

IN OSLO, I SAVE A NUN FROM A COLLAPSING WALL.

IN PARIS, I STOP A NINE-YEAR-OLD FROM FALLING OFF THE EIFFEL TOWER.

IN GLASGOW, I RAID A SUPERMARKET SO CHILDREN IN THE GHETTO CAN HAVE A MEAL.

DOES THIS CONSTITUTE STEALING IF THE WORLD'S ABOUT TO END? MAYBE.

BUT LET THESE KIDS DIE WITH FULL STOMACHS.

MAYBE DAD'LL COME ACROSS THEM ON HIS ROUNDS.

MAYBE HE'LL HEAR.

KID FLASH!

KID FLASH!

KID FLASH!

MEANWHILE, I TRY TO GET *BARRY* OUT OF MY MIND.

AND I *FAIL.*

WHAT'S HE *DOING* WITH ONE DAY LEFT? GETTING *DRUNK?* GETTING *LUCKY?*

ROCKING *OUT?* LEARNING THE *KEYBOARD* AND THE *BASS GUITAR?*

INDULGING HIS EVERY STUPID *WHIM* TO THE *MAX* WHILE THE REST OF THE WORLD *SUFFERS?*

SURE HE IS.

WHY SHOULD *TODAY* BE DIFFERENT FROM ANY *OTHER* DAY FOR HIM?

DAMN IT! I'M *NOT* LETTING HIM GET *AWAY* WITH THAT!

I'LL FIND HIM! I'LL MAKE *HIM* BE RESPONSIBLE!

THAT'LL *SHOW* DAD!

SEVENTY PRECIOUS MINUTES LATER, I'VE COMBED EUROPE AND SOUTH AMERICA. BY THE TIME I HIT NORTH AFRICA, I'M READY TO GIVE UP.

AND THEN--

HEY! HEY! THAT TICKLES!

--I HEAR HIS VOICE.

BARRY?

OH.

IT'S YOU.

I-I--

YOU TELL ME WE HAVE A SHORT TIME TO LIVE--AND THEN YOU SPEND IT LIKE THIS?

I KNOW. IT'S TAKING HOURS. BEAUTIFUL, ISN'T IT?

MEHMET HERE REALLY KNOWS HIS ART.

I BOW IN APPRECIATION OF YOUR COMPLIMENTING.

MAN, YOU LOOK WASHED. BEEN LOOKING FOR ME? I BET YOU THOUGHT I'D BE DASHING AROUND THE GLOBE--HAVING FUN, TRYING NEW EXPERIENCES--

PLEASE TO HOLD STILL.

--CRAMMING A WHOLE LIFE INTO ONE SINGLE DAY AT THE SPEED OF LIGHT. AM I RIGHT?

IT CROSSED MY MIND.

WHY BOTHER?

IF I'VE GOT ONE DAY LEFT... BY GOD...

...I'M GONNA WASTE IT AS I SEE FIT.

WHY? SO DADDY CAN BE PROUD OF HIS LITTLE GIRL?

SIGN YOUR WORK, DID YOU?

SAME WAY YOU ALWAYS MAKE SURE YOUR FOOD-DELIVERY ROUTE ALWAYS "SOMEHOW" MANAGES TO INTERSECT HIS?

THAT'S NOT TRUE--

IT'S ABSOLUTELY TRUE! ASK YOURSELF WHY YOU'RE DRESSED UP IN THAT SUIT, KIDDO!

DON'T YOU GET IT? NOBODY CARES ABOUT THE SO-CALLED "FLASH LEGACY!"

YOU'RE LYING!

DAD TALKS ABOUT RESPONSIBILITY ALL THE TIME, BUT HE JUST USES THAT AS AN EXCUSE!

AN EXCUSE TO RUN AWAY FROM US 'CAUSE HE DOESN'T KNOW WHAT TO DO WITH US! THAT'S HOW HE'S ALWAYS DEALT WITH HIS PROBLEMS... BY RUNNING!

THAT'S NOT--

IT IS! SIS, YOU DON'T CARE ABOUT THIS LEGACY BUSINESS ANY MORE THAN I DO! ADMIT IT! THE ONLY REASON YOU WEAR THE COSTUME IS TO BE NOTICED!

TO GET HIS APPROVAL!

NO! NO!

YES! JESUS! THE ONLY TRUTHFUL, FUNCTIONING PERSON IN THIS WHOLE FAMILY--

--THE ONLY ONE WHO DOES ANYTHING HONESTLY--

--IS ME!

YOU DON'T HAVE TO SAY ANYTHING. OF *COURSE* I'M RIGHT.

NOW... WHAT ARE YOU GONNA *DO* ABOUT IT?

SO I *TOLD* HIM.

AND FOR THE FIRST TIME IN *YEARS*, HE ACTUALLY HAD AN *EXPRESSION* ON HIS FACE.

WOW. NOT TOO LATE FOR A *TATTOO* BEFORE YOU'RE OFF, Y'KNOW. GOT JUST THE ONE PICKED *OUT* FOR YOU--A *STRUTTING PEACOCK*. MEHMET CAN GET YOU *IN* AND--

--OUT--?

HONESTLY.

THE *ENERGY* I PUT *INTO* THAT KID...

MEHMET?

SIT! I FIX, BUT IT WILL TAKE TIME! TAKE *MUCH* TIME!

COOL.

IRIS?

IRIS?

SHE'S NOT THERE.

÷SIGH÷

MAN, IT IS IMPOSSIBLE TO GET WASTED WITH THIS METABOLISM...

BARRY? WHAT ARE YOU DOING HERE?

NOT BAD, AND YOU? WHERE'S IRIS?

BARRY?

PLANET KRYPTON

Barry Kitson

"I'VE BEEN WAITRESSING FOR ABOUT SIX MONTHS."

SO, ROSE... TELL ME WHY YOU WANT TO WORK HERE.

PLANET KRYPTON

I... COULDN'T SAY, MR. GOLD. I JUST--

MR. CARTER. OR, BETTER YET, MICHAEL. PLEASE.

"BOOSTER GOLD" WAS A JUSTICE LEAGUER... AND, FOR THE MOMENT, I'M IN SEMI-RETIRE-MENT, AT LEAST. UNTIL PLANET KRYPTON TAKES OFF--AND IT WILL.

PEOPLE LOVE THEME RESTAURANTS, AND WE ROTATE THE LARGEST REVOLVING STOCK OF SUPER-HERO MEMORA-BILIA IN THE WORLD. EVEN I CAN'T KEEP UP WITH EVERYTHING WE'VE GOT.

PLANET KRYPTON

"MR. CARTER, THE OWNER, SEEMED LIKE A GENUINELY PLEASANT MAN..."

DON'T GET ME WRONG. I LIKE TO KEEP SOMEWHAT ACTIVE AS A CRIMEFIGHTER. AS WE USED TO SAY IN THE JLA, THERE'S ALWAYS A KITTEN IN A TREE SOME-WHERE. BUT FOR NOW...

...WELL... ENJOY THE JOB, ROSE. IF YOU HAVE ANY QUESTIONS, JUST ASK.

I THINK YOU'LL FIND THE WAITSTAFF HERE AS FRIENDLY AND HELPFUL AS THEIR NAMESAKES.

"...IF NOT NECESSARILY THE GREATEST JUDGE OF CHARACTER."

WHAT **IS** IT?

I--I THINK THAT'S **MY** CHEESEBURG--

THEN WAIT FOR THE **NEXT** ONE. APPARENTLY, **MY** TABLE IS LATE FOR HER **PEDICURE**, LA DE DAH.

YOU WANT **FAST** DON'T ASK ME SIX TIMES WHAT'S IN THE **COBB SALAD**, YOU FRIGGIN'...

"YOU'D THINK, GIVEN THE ROLES THEY **PLAY**, THE PEOPLE **WORKING** HERE WOULD BE A LITTLE MORE **NOBLE**... MORE **RESPONSIBLE**..."

MISS, HAVE YOU SEEN OUR **WAITER?**

WHICH ONE IS--

BATMAN?

I'LL--I'LL **LOOK**--

"...BUT EVEN WHEN THEY **TRY** TO BE NICE..."

HERO DIAL

...THOUGHT MAYBE WE COULD GRAB A **MOVIE** OR SOMETHING...?

LET ME... LET ME THINK ABOUT IT, JEFF.

"...THEY DON'T TRY VERY HARD."

OF **COURSE** SHE TURNED YOU DOWN, MAN. SHE'S A COLD FISH. "FISH." GET IT?

YEAH. WE GOT IT.

I MADE A **FISH** JOKE.

AGAIN. IT WAS FUNNY THE FIRST THIRTY TIMES. STILL, JEFF, YOU CAN DO BETTER THAN **ROSE!** C'MON!

WHO'D WANNA GO OUT WITH **HER?**

"I HAD AN OPPORTUNITY TO BE NOBLE ONCE...TO BE A HERO."

PLANET KRYPTON

'NIGHT, ROSE. YOU NEED A RIDE *HOME?*

NAH. 'NIGHT, *JEFF.*

CLOSED

"FAILED."

STOREROOM

KLIK

BEANS

BEANS

BEANS

SO WHO'M I TO THROW *STONES,* RIGHT?

MAYBE I FIT RIGHT *IN* WITH *THIS* CROWD.

ONE CHANCE I *HAD...WHY* COULDN'T *I* HAVE DONE THE RIGHT THING?

TELL ME.

PLEASE.

HAUNTED

MARK WAID-writer
BARRY KITSON-art
KEN LOPEZ-letters
PAT GARRAHY-colors
JAMISON-separations
TONY BEDARD-associate editor
DAN RASPLER-editor

Based on
KINGDOM COME
by MARK WAID
and ALEX ROSS

THEY DIDN'T, OF COURSE. THEY *NEVER* DO.

SOMETIMES, FOR A BRIEF SECOND, I FEEL AS IF THEY *ACKNOWLEDGE* MY PRESENCE--

LAS
TRI

--BUT THEN THEY DRIFT *AWAY* LIKE THE GHOSTS THEY *ARE.*

NO ONE KNOWS ABOUT THEM BUT *ME.* I CAME ACROSS THEM NOT LONG AFTER I *STARTED* HERE, THE NIGHT I VOLUN- TEERED TO *LOCK UP.*

AT FIRST, THEY *SCARED* ME...BUT WE *METROPOLI- TANS* ARE PRETTY HARD TO *STARTLE* AFTER DEALING WITH *DOOMSDAY* AND *MIX...MYXY...MYZ...*

...*WHATEVER.*

CLEARLY, THESE SPIRITS MEANT NO *HARM.* THEY'RE NOT ANY SUPER-HEROES I'VE EVER READ ABOUT IN THE *MAGAZINES* OR SEEN ON TV...

...BUT THEY MAKE ME FEEL *SAFE,* JUST THE *SAME.*

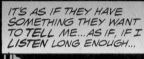

IT'S AS IF THEY HAVE SOMETHING THEY WANT TO *TELL* ME...AS IF, IF I *LISTEN* LONG ENOUGH...

...THEY'LL *HEAR* ME, TOO.

IT GETS HARD TO EXPLAIN TO THE OTHER WAITERS WHY I'M *HERE* SO MANY NIGHTS. SOMETIMES I HAVE TO TAMPER WITH THE WORK SCHEDULES BEFORE THEY GET POSTED.

AT FIRST, I WAS AFRAID OF GETTING CAUGHT BY WHOEVER *OPENED UP...* UNTIL I TOOK TO HIDING OUT IN THE *RESTROOM* AND MINGLING IN WITH THE *LUNCH RUSH*.

I WASH WHAT CLOTHES I *HAVE* ON THE CHANGE OF *TIPS* AND SEND THE *PAYCHECKS* BACK *HOME*. I'M SURE MOTHER CAN USE THE *MONEY* EVEN THOUGH I'M NOT *HOME* ANYMORE.

I HAVE OTHER HIDING PLACES. BEHIND THE STARRO IS ONE. NO ONE CATCHES ME. NO ONE NOTICES ME MUCH AT *ALL*.

I COULDN'T *STAY* THERE.

I NEVER CHEAT ANYONE OUT OF THEIR *HOURS*, BUT THE AFTERNOON SHIFT DOES ME NO *GOOD*, SO...

WHICH IS THE WAY I *LIKE* IT.

NOT *AFTER*.

OH, GREAT. I DIDN'T KNOW *VERA* LIVED THIS CLOSE BY.

IF I'M *LUCKY,* MAYBE ALL SHE'LL DO IS *SNEER* AT ME.

OR *NOT.*

HEY, ROSE. SMALL *WORLD.*

SAY, LISTEN. JAMAL NEEDS TO TRADE SHIFTS WITH SOMEBODY THURSDAY. CAN *YOU* SWAP?

AFTERNOON? GEE, I DON'T--

AW, C'MON. HE'S GOTTA GET HIS BROTHER TO *TREATMENT.*

TREATMENT?

'SHYEA. HIS BROTHER'S IN THE LAST STAGES OF *AIDS.* JAMAL'S HIS *NURSE.* YOU *KNEW* THAT, RIGHT?

NO.

I HAVE AN *UNCLE* WHO'S GAY, SO I'M CURIOUS TO HEAR MORE *ABOUT* THIS. OVER THE NEXT FEW DAYS, I KEEP MY *EARS* OPEN...

...AND I LEARN *OTHER* THINGS AS WELL.

174

RUSSELL TAKES THE RESTAURANT **LEFTOVERS** TO A SHELTER.

STARK IS A VOLUNTEER **FIREFIGHTER.**

LINDA'S RAISING THREE KIDS ON HER **OWN**--TWO SONS AND A **FOSTER** CHILD.

TATE KICKED A **HEROIN HABIT** BY THE STRENGTH OF HIS OWN **WILL.**

I NEVER WOULD HAVE **GUESSED.** ON THE JOB, THEY CAN BE AS SMALL AND PETTY AS THE **WORST** PEOPLE...

...BUT IT'S LIKE ALL OF THEM HAVE THEIR OWN LITTLE **SECRET IDENTITIES.**

LIKE THEY'RE ALL HEROES IN THEIR OWN WAY.

WHICH LEAVES ME MORE ALONE THAN **EVER...**

MISS, DO WE EVEN **HAVE A WAITER?**

IT'S **BATMAN'S** TABLE, SIR. I'LL TRY TO FIND HIM. I'M SORRY.

THAT NIGHT, I WATCH THE GHOSTS BEGIN APPEARING IN GREATER NUMBERS. MEN WITH **RIPPLING MUSCLES.** WOMEN IN CAPES AND TIGHTS...

...ALL AS SILENT AS THEY ARE BEAUTIFUL.

HE **SWORE** TO ME THAT A **NEW LIFE** WOULD START THE DAY WE WERE **MARRIED**... THAT I'D **KNOW** IT BECAUSE HE'D MAKE **SURE NOBODY** IN MY FAMILY WOULD EVER HAVE TO WORK **AGAIN**, LEAST OF ALL, **ME**.

A MAN WITH **AMBITION**, MY MOTHER CALLED HIM. "A **MOVER** AND A **SHAKER**, GONNA BE SOMEBODY **BIG**."

MOM WAS DISAPPOINTED, BUT TO HER CREDIT, SHE DIDN'T **SAY** MUCH.

SIS, ON THE OTHER HAND...

AND THEN I WENT AND TOLD HIM "**NO**."

I JUST... I DIDN'T FEEL...

...CONNECTED...

WHAT'S THE **MATTER** WITH YOU? HOW CAN YOU BE SO **SELFISH**?

MARY, I...I DON'T **LOVE** HIM.

YOU DON'T ALWAYS GET *MARRIED* FOR *LOVE*, ROSIE! THE GUY'S GONNA BE A *MILLIONAIRE* SIX MONTHS FROM NOW! YOU WANT MOM TO WORK UNTIL SHE'S IN HER *GRAVE?*

MARY, I *WANT* TO TRUST HIM, *REALLY*, BUT... YOU WANT ME TO GET MARRIED FOR THE *MONEY?* WHAT IF IT'S ALL A *PIPE DREAM?* WHAT IF I'M NO BETTER OFF A *YEAR* FROM NOW THAN I AM *TODAY?*

YOU'RE *BOUND* T'BE! HE'S GOT A *CELLPHONE* 'N' STUFF, HE'S *ALWAYS* HUSTLIN', EVERYBODY *KNOWS* HIM. HE'S A *MOVER!* LISTEN TO YOUR *FAMILY!*

LOOK *NOBODY'S* ASKIN' YA TO GET *HURT* OR NOTHIN'! IF HE WERE A *CREEP*— OKAY! BUT HE TREATS YOU *NICE*, AND... AND..

ROSE, YOU GOTTA GET *REAL.* WHO *ELSE* IS GONNA COME *ALONG* F'R YOU?

F'R *US?*

NOW, EVERY SINGLE DAY, I THINK ABOUT HOW *RIGHT* SHE WAS. ABOUT HOW I HAD A CHANCE TO MAKE THINGS FINALLY WORK *OUT* FOR MY *FAMILY*...AND COULDN'T DO IT.

THEY WERE *COUNTING* ON ME TO BE *THEIR* HERO... AND I LET THEM *DOWN*

HAVING TRADED FOR JAMAL'S AFTERNOON SHIFT, I HAD TO SPEND THE NEXT NIGHT AT THE "Y"!

THE FOLLOWING EVENING, I FOUND OUT JUST HOW MUCH I'D MISSED...

BOSS'S OFFICE.

CHECK.

...YES, I KNOW THIS ISN'T EXACTLY YOUR FIELD OF EXPERTISE, BUT...

...YES, I KNOW GOTHAM'S YOUR TOP PRIORITY, BUT...

...LOOK. FOR OLD TIMES' SAKE. WE WERE JLA TEAMMATES. REMEMBER THAT TIME WITH AMAZO? YEAH?

WELL, I'M CALLING IN THAT FAVOR. I NEED THE WORLD'S GREATEST DETECTIVE TO INVESTIGATE A BREAK-IN.

WELL, WHAT ELSE WOULD I CALL IT? I TOLD YOU. I SAW THEM LAST NIGHT WITH MY OWN EYES.

GHOSTS.

THE RESTAURANT'S CRAWLING WITH THEM.

YES, I'LL STAY OUT OF YOUR WAY. YES, GHOST-BUSTING IS FOR SOMEONE WHO BELIEVES IN THE SUPERNATURAL.

BUT WHATEVER'S GOING ON AFTER HOURS HERE, I FIGURE I CAN COUNT ON YOU OF ALL PEOPLE TO PUT A STOP TO IT.

JUST LET ME KNOW WHAT YOU UNCOVER, AND TOGETHER WE'LL--

EXCUSE ME. ROSE? CAN YOU BRING SALT?

ROSE?

ROSE?

RECORDING. INITIAL OBSERVATION: THE ESTABLISHMENT IS EVERYTHING BOOSTER *CLAIMED* IT WOULD BE...

...AND, PERHAPS, *MORE.*

AMIDST THE TAWDRY TOYS AND *WELL-KNOWN* TRINKETS SERVING AS *DECORATION,* THERE ARE PIECES UNIQUELY...

... *IMAGINATIVE.*

WHAT'S *DOUBLY* PUZZLING ABOUT THESE ITEMS IS NOT MERELY THEIR *UNFAMILIARITY...*

THANAGARIAN ABSORBASCON

...BUT THEIR MYSTERIOUS *ABSENCE* FROM THE RESTAURANT'S *STOCK INVOICES* AND *INVENTORY,* AS INDICATED ON MY *UPLINK.*

PHANTOM ZONE PROJECTOR

FURTHER NOTATION: BOOSTER'S REPLICA OF THE RADIOACTIVE XENO-MINERAL *KRYPTONITE* HAS BEEN INTEGRATED INTO A DISPLAY OF *SIMILAR* PIECES...

RYPTONITE K

...UNACCOUNTABLY COLORED IN *FANCIFUL HUES.*

HOW *BIZARRE.*

 SECOND MYSTERY: UPON EXAMINATION... PARTICULARLY UPON *HANDLING*...

...I FIND THAT SOME OF THE ITEMS IN QUESTION EVOKE AN INEXPLICABLE *EMOTIONAL* SENSATION.

THE CLOSEST DESCRIPTIVE *ASSIGNABLE* WOULD SEEM TO BE "*NOSTALGIA*"--BUT AS THESE THINGS DO NOT, *CANNOT EXIST*...

...*NOSTALGIA* CANNOT *POSSIBLY* APPLY TO THAT WHICH CANNOT BE RIGHTFULLY...

...REMEMBERED...

KATHY..?

IN THAT MOMENT, HIS VOICE TURNS SOFT... AND SOMEHOW I KNOW IT SURPRISES HIM AS MUCH AS IT SURPRISES ME.

THEN WHAT HAPPENS NEXT...

Krr KKK

...SURPRISES BOTH OF US!

HOLD IT RIGHT THERE!

=GASP!=

YOU...YOU KNEW I WAS HERE...?

FROM THE MOMENT I ENTERED. I SIMPLY ASSUMED YOU WERE ONE OF THE EPHEMERAL SPIRITS BOOSTER COMPLAINED ABOUT.

WHAT? WHY WOULD YOU THINK--?

BECAUSE YOU CARRY YOURSELF LIKE ONE. EXPLAIN YOURSELF.

MY... MY NAME IS ROSE, I'M... I DON'T KNOW WHAT'S GOING ON HERE, EITHER. I'M JUST A WAITRESS HERE...

THEN YOU PICKED A *POOR NIGHT* TO WORK *OVERTIME.* YOU WANT TO BE A *HERO,* BE A HERO TO *YOURSELF.*

GO HOME.

HE GOES BACK TO THE TONE OF VOICE THAT COULD COMMAND *KINGS*... AND YET, SOMEHOW I FIND THE COURAGE TO TELL HIM--

I--I *CAN'T.* NOT *YET,* NOT UNTIL I *KNOW* MORE ABOUT THE *GHOSTS.*

I WOULDN'T CALL THEM *GHOSTS.* THEY MAY, HOWEVER, BE *ECHOES*... AS UNLIKELY AS IT *SOUNDS,* REFLECTIONS OF REALITIES *SIMILAR* TO OUR *OWN,* THOUGH *DIVERGENT.*

IS THAT WHY YOU *RECOGNIZED* THAT *WOMAN?*

I DON'T *KNOW* HER.

BUT *YOU--*

IT'S *IMPOSSIBLE* FOR ME TO KNOW HER. GO *HOME...* *NOW.* THIS IS *DANGEROUS* TERRITORY.

THE ECHOES ARE *HERE,* IN THIS PLACE, BECAUSE SOMETHING--OR SOMEONE--IS WEAKENING THE WALLS *BETWEEN* THEIR REALITIES AND *OURS*--

--AND I THINK I KNOW *WHO!*

AAAAH! DON'T *SHOOT!* WE'RE *GOOD GUYS!* WE COME IN *PEACE!*

QUIET, OFFSPRING. NIGHTSTAR, KID FLASH-- *FREE* US FROM THESE BONDS.

WELL *PLAYED,* DETECTIVE. WHAT GAVE US *AWAY?*

THE *WRISTBANDS.* YOU FOUR ARE THE ONLY "GHOSTS" *WEARING* THEM.

THOUGH THEY GAVE YOU A WRAITHLIKE *APPEARANCE,* I NOTICED YOUR "*KID FLASH*" WAS CLEARLY *CORPOREAL.*

YOUR *INTERFERENCE* IN OUR AFFAIRS ISN'T EXACTLY *WELCOME.* WHAT *BROUGHT* YOU?

I'LL ASK THE QUESTIONS. WHAT'S *YOUR* RELATIONSHIP TO THE *WRAITHS?*

THEY SEEM TO BE A *SIDE EFFECT* OF OUR *PRESENCE* HERE AND WHAT WE'RE *DOING.* WE'RE HERE TO--

NO. IF HE'S WORTHY OF HIS *REPUTATION,* HE CAN TELL *US* OUR MISSION.

IBN, *DON'T.* WE HAVEN'T TIME FOR *GAMES!*

WELL, DETECTIVE?

YOUR FRIEND IS *CORRECT.*

...

THAT'S *ALL* YOU HAVE TO *SAY?*

THAT'S *IT?*

IB? IB, WHATTAYA *DOIN'?*

REFUSING TO *REWARD* HIS OVER-RATED REPUTATION WITH *EASY* ANSWERS.

HE'LL KNOW WHY WE CAME...WHEN THE TIME IS *RIGHT...*

KWKMMMM

...AND A ROSE D'ANGELO WHO GAVE IN FOR HER *FAMILY*...

...AND CHANGED *NOTHING.*

BATMAN TOLD ME TO BE A HERO TO *MYSELF.* FOR THE FIRST TIME IN A *YEAR,* I FINALLY *REALIZE*...

...MAYBE I ALREADY *HAD* BEEN.

EITHER WAY, I DECIDE I'M A LITTLE TOO *BUSY* TO BE HAUNTED BY THE *PAST* ANYMORE.

I HAVE TO GET HOME.

TO BE
CONTINUED

Mike Zeck/John Beatty

--WHERE, MOMENTS AGO, A BLAST OF *INCALCULABLE POWER* SWEPT ACROSS KANSAS, AS WELL AS PARTS OF *NEBRASKA, IOWA* AND *MISSOURI.*

EXCUSE ME...

...PARDON ME...

CASUALTIES CURRENTLY NUMBER IN THE *TENS* OF *THOUSANDS*, WITH FURTHER TALLIES ESCALATING BY THE *MINUTE.*

EARLY REPORTS INDICATE THAT THE HERO *CAPTAIN ATOM* WAS PRESENT AT THE SCENE, BATTLING THE AS-YET-UNIDENTIFIED *FIGURE* WHO *SPARKED* THIS TRAGEDY!

THOUGH THE *IDENTITY* OF THAT ASSAILANT HAS YET TO BE *CONFIRMED*, THIS REPORTER IS AMAZED... AND, FRANKLY, *FRIGHTENED*...TO REPORT...

...THAT THE SATELLITE *PHOTOS* WHICH REVEAL THE *HUNDRED-MILE PATH* AND *PATTERN* OF THE KANSAS *BLAST*...

MIGHTY RIVERS

MARK WAID
WRITER
MIKE ZECK
PENCILS
JOHN BEATTY
INKS
PHIL FELIX
LETTERS
JOHN KALISZ
COLORS
DIGITAL CHAMELEON
SEPARATIONS
TONY BEDARD
ASSOC. EDITOR
DAN RASPLER
EDITOR

BASED ON *KINGDOM COME* BY
MARK WAID & ALEX ROSS

SUPERMAN CREATED BY
JERRY SIEGEL & JOE SHUSTER

--CAN'T BELIEVE HUNTER BETRAYED US LIKE THAT--

--DON'T KNOW WHAT HE WAS THINKING--

--SHOULD NEVER HAVE ADOPTED HIM INTO THE LINEAR MEN--

THIS IS RISKY.

DON'T WORRY. THEY CAN'T DETECT OUR PRESENCE--NOT EVEN HERE IN THEIR OWN HEADQUARTERS!

I'VE PHASE-SHIFTED US IN BETWEEN ATOSECONDS.

--NEVER!

LIRI, GET ME THE WAVERIDER OF TEN YEARS FROM NOW. WE'LL NEED HIS EXPERIENCE.

GOOD. YOU HAVE TO HIDE THE TRUTH FROM THEM, HUNTER. IF THEY LEARN WHAT WE KNOW--

--THEY'LL WORK OVERTIME TO ELIMINATE IT--PROVIDED THEY CAN EVEN ACCEPT IT. BELIEVE ME, I'M WELL AWARE OF THAT!

RIGHT AWAY, WAVE-RIDER.

GOG CONTINUES HIS MAD RAMPAGE TOWARDS THE 20TH CENTURY. FORTUNATELY, OUR FAIL-SAFE IS IN PLACE--THANKS TO THE AGENTS I DISPATCHED THROUGH HYPER-TIME TO GATHER SUPPLIES.

--WIELDS IT FAR MORE CAPRICIOUSLY AND DISASTROUSLY. IT WAS A SMALL RISK COMPARED TO THE MUCH GREATER ONE--

--OF EXPOSING THE MOST REMARKABLE SECRET IN HUMAN HISTORY.

WHAT? YOU GAVE THEM THE POWER TO--

I LENT THEM THE POWER ... AND THEY NO MORE KNOW ITS TRUE POTENTIAL AND SIGNIFICANCE THAN DOES GOG, WHO-- AS WE HAVE SEEN--

THRAKT

MA! PA! ARE YOU--

Shhh! WE'RE OKAY, SON. JUST A FEW BURNS. YOUR FATHER'S RESTING. HE WAS MORE EXPOSED.

TO WHAT? WHAT HAPPENED? MY GOD...THOUSANDS OF INNOCENT PEOPLE...

WHAT CAUSED THIS?

WE SURE DON'T KNOW, CLARK. IT WAS... GOOD LORD, IT WAS AS IF THE SKY ITSELF HAD CAUGHT FIRE FOR A SECOND.

IT LIKE TO'VE TORN THE SKIN OFF US WHEN THE SHOCK-WAVE HIT.

FOR A MOMENT, WE WERE AFRAID SOMEONE HAD FINALLY DROPPED THE BOMB.

CLARK, WE'RE NOT... I MEAN... THERE WAS NO RADIATION, WAS THERE...?

NONE THAT MY MICROSCOPIC VISION CAN DETECT, MA. YOU'RE SAFE, BUT--

JUST OVER THE HORIZON.

I SEE SOMETHING.

CLARK?

SON, WHAT IS IT?

FOR WHAT I AM ABOUT TO *DO*, THE WORLD WILL *FORGIVE* ME THOSE FEW SLAIN BY MY *INITIAL BLAZE*... AS *WELL* AS THOSE WHO ARE *ABOUT* TO DIE.

YOU ARE NOT *ONE* OF THEM, INCIDENTALLY. YOU DON'T ESCAPE THAT *EASILY*.

THIS TIME... *UNLIKE* ALL THE *OTHER* TIMES...

OTHER--? WHAT OTH--

NNNGH!

...I'M NOT GOING TO *KILL* YOU.

THIS TIME... WITH THE "HELP" OF CAPTAIN ATOM'S NUCLEAR ENERGY... I'M GOING TO ACCELERATE THE TRUE KANSAS CATACLYSM...

...MAKE IT HAPPEN *TODAY*, TWENTY YEARS *AHEAD* OF SCHEDULE...

...IN SUCH A MANNER THAT *EVERYONE* WILL FINALLY REALIZE THAT *YOU* ARE *RESPONSIBLE* FOR HISTORY'S *GREATEST* TRAGEDY. THAT'S WHY I SIGNED YOUR *NAME* TO IT.

SO EVERYONE WILL *FOREVER KNOW* THE *DEPTH* OF THE *SECRET, UNGODLY EVIL* YOU CLOAK BENEATH THAT FACADE OF *HEROISM* AND *LEADERSHIP*.

SO THAT THEY WILL *KNOW* YOU AS THE *ULTIMATE CORRUPTOR* OF *BIBLICAL LEGEND*...

... THE *WINGED BEAST* CAST OUT OF THE *HEAVENS* LIKE A *FALLING STAR*, IDENTIFIED BY A *UNIQUE SIGIL*.

WHAT I *DO* TODAY...

-- I TAKE IT CAPTAIN ATOM'S STILL UNCONSCIOUS, BUT SAFE. ANY MOVEMENT FROM THE ENEMY?

ONLY A SMILE. HE'S TOYING WITH US...

"I DON'T KNOW WHERE HE FOUND KRYPTONITE, BUT CLEARLY HE'S ANXIOUS TO USE IT."

TELL US... WHAT DID GOG MEAN WHEN HE CLAIMED SUPERMAN WAS RESPONSIBLE FOR "HISTORY'S GREATEST TRAGEDY"?

WHAT HE... WHAT HE WAS REFERRING TO... WAS THE TERRIBLE COST PAID THE DAY I--

GOG IS A MADMAN. LEAVE IT AT THAT. CLARK, WE MUST ACT.

AND DO WHAT, DIANA? THIS LOOKED LIKE A JOB FOR SUPERMAN...

...BUT WHATEVER I DO... WE LOSE.

GOG HAS ALREADY CHANGED THE FUTURE SIMPLY BY BEING HERE. ANY WRONG MOVE WILL ALMOST CERTAINLY ERASE US AND ALL WE KNOW FROM REALITY--

--BUT WE MUST STRIKE TO SAVE THE PEOPLE OF KANSAS--AND OUR SON, IN THE HOPE HE'LL EVEN STILL EXIST--

--THOUGH I STILL CAN'T FATHOM WHERE GOG MIGHT HAVE HIDDEN...

...HIM...

OH, MY GOD. JONATHAN...!

GOG PUT HIM INSIDE THE KRYPTONITE!

THAT WON'T *HOLD* HIM! I CAN ALREADY HEAR IT *CRACKING*!

BUT IT *BOUGHT* US *TIME* FOR A *RESCUE*. GO. GO!

HOW *IS* HE? IF CAPTAIN *ATOM'S* VITAL SIGNS ARE STABLE, I'D SUGGEST--

I'VE SIGNALLED THE *JLA* TO *COME* FOR HIM.

THEY'LL BACK US *UP* ONCE THEY FINISH HELPING THE VICTIMS GOG *SACRIFICED* TO MAKE HIS *STATE*-MENT.

I HAVE IT UNDER *CONTROL*.

OF COURSE YOU DO.

YOU KNOW, YOU REALLY OUGHT TO LEARN TO *RELAX* A TINY BIT. YOU'LL *SURVIVE* IT.

I *DID*...

OH, THANK THE *GODS*! HE'S *SAFE*! BRUCE, IS HE--?

HE SEEMS ALL RIGHT. CLARK'S BUILT UP SOME *IMMUNITY* TO KRYPTONITE OVER THE YEARS. MAYBE HE PASSED THAT ALONG TO LITTLE *JONATHAN*.

IN ANY EVENT, HE'S A *SURVIVOR*, JUST LIKE HIS--

NO.

NO!

NOOOOOO!

FOR NOTHING. WE FOUGHT...FOR NOTHING.

IT'S HAPPENING. OUR TIMELINE IS FADING.

OUR CHILD...OUR CHILD IS GONE...AND WITH HIM, EVERYTHING WE KNOW OF OUR WORLD.

"OUR"...CHILD...? BUT...

...I...I DON'T UNDERSTAND ANY OF THIS...

IT DOESN'T MATTER. NOTHING DOES. NOT ANYMORE.

WE CANNOT BE LONG FOR THE WORLD. SOON, WE TOO WILL BE BUT... BUT MEMORIES.

BUT I SWEAR BY ALL THAT THE GODS WILL ALLOW...

...WE WILL NOT GO QUIETLY FROM THIS GOOD EARTH...

...WITHOUT FIRST TASTING VENGEANCE.

I SEE YOU'RE STILL WEARING THE *ARMBANDS* I GAVE YOU. THAT EXPLAINS WHY YOU'RE STILL *HERE.* GOOD.

GOG'S ON HIS WAY. BE *READY.*

WE'VE STAYED TO DO OUR PART, HUNTER.

THE FUTURE IS *OURS...* AND WE WILL *KEEP* IT THAT WAY AT ALL *COSTS.*

THEN WE'VE FOUND THE *RIGHT* ALLIES. WHO *ARE* THEY, SUPERMAN?

MEET *KID FLASH,* THE DAUGHTER OF *FLASH...*

...*OFFSPRING,* THE SON OF *PLASTIC MAN...*

...AND *NIGHTSTAR* AND *IBN AL XU'FFASCH,* THE CHILDREN OF...

...WELL... LET'S JUST SAY OF FRIENDS VERY *FAMILIAR.*

UNDER MY *DIRECTION,* THEY'VE BEEN HARD AT WORK.

GREAT *HERA.* AT EVERY *TURN,* THIS BECOMES MORE *AMAZING...*

...AND MORE *DANGEROUS,* HUNTER, I KNOW THIS PLACE.

YOU CAN'T SERIOUSLY EXPECT US TO STAGE A SHOWDOWN IN THE *HEART* OF METROPOLIS.

NOT FOR A *MOMENT.* FOR THE PROTECTION OF THE CITY *OUTSIDE,* EFFECTIVE *INSTANTLY...*

"...I'M PLUNGING THIS BUILDING INTO HYPER-TIME."

PLANET KRYPTON

CLOSED

TITANS?

LOOK OUT! HIS STAFF--

URCHINS.

--IS SOMETHING I'VE HAD QUITE ENOUGH OF!

YOU HONESTLY BELIEVE I MIGHT SURRENDER IT?

FOOL.

IT IS AN ARTIFACT OF UNIMAGINABLE FORCE... HOUSING THE EMERALD ENERGY OF THE GUARDIANS OF THE UNIVERSE...

...THE COSMIC POWER OF THE SOURCE...

...AND THE MAGICAL MIGHT OF ZEUS AND SHAZAM COMBINED!

YOU HAVE NO WEAPON TO EQUAL IT.

NOT ONE.

BATMAN, HE'S WRONG! HUNTER GATHERED THE FOUR OF US KIDS FOR A REASON! HE HAD US--

HE HAD YOU STOCKING THE ARENA--

--PIECE BY IMPOSSIBLE PIECE.

THIS ISN'T A RESTAURANT.

PHANTOM ZONE PROJECTOR

IT'S AN ARSENAL.

NYAAARGH!

GREEN ARROW BOW & QUIVER

EN LANTERN VER RINGS

GAS GUN

SANDMAN

JONA HEX

WELL DONE-- BUT ONCE AGAIN YOU UNDERESTIMATE THE LIMITS OF MY INVULNERABILITY!

I WILL NOT BE BANISHED BY A SIMPLE DIMENSIONAL TRANS- PORTER!

YOU ACCOMPLISHED NOTHING WITH YOUR PATHETIC GAMBIT, BATMAN!

NOT TRUE

ZZZASH!

HE KEEPS SAYING THAT! FOR WHAT, GOG?

FOR WHAT AM I RESPONSIBLE?

DON'T WORRY ABOUT IT! THESE NEXT FEW SECONDS ARE CRITICAL!

FOR THE FIRST TIME, WE'VE GOT HIM ON THE ROPES!

YOU MUST--

YEAAARGH!

--MUST BE HELD--

--HELD ACCOUNTABLE --FOR YOUR SINS!

I HAVE A MISSION! I CANNOT SQUANDER MY POWER!

I HAVE HAD

ENOUGH

I SEE I'VE... BROKEN YOUR TOYS.

YOU'RE FINISHED. I... AM NOT.

FOR WHAT I --

--FOR WHAT THE WORLD HAS ENDURED -- WILL ENDURE --

-- I WILL SLAY SUPERMAN... EVEN IF I MUST EXPEND EVERY LAST REMNANT OF MY LIFEFORCE TO DO SO.

SO SHALL ...

... SO SHALL WE PROTECT HIM.

IF YOU WANT HIM, GOG...

...YOU'LL HAVE TO GO THROUGH US...

DIANA, NO! DON'T --

AAAAGH!

THAT'S... IT. DON'T... SURRENDER...

CAN'T... MOVE...

PUSH.

I... I CAN'T...

...

YOU HAVE TO, KAL.

WHEN GOG SAID YOU WERE RESPONSIBLE FOR A GREAT TRAGEDY...

...HE WAS RIGHT.

MY WRISTBAND--!

CHZAAK!

IT COULDN'T SAVE US, SON! WE'VE ALREADY CHANGED TOO MUCH HISTORY!

OUR FUTURE'S GONE--AND WE WILL BE TOO--

--IF THIS DOESN'T KILL US FIRST!

GOOD RIDDANCE TO FOUL APOSTLES, THEN.

I DID IT.

THE DEVIL'S FINALLY IN HIS HELL. I WON.

IT COST ME EVERY-THING, BUT I WON! I...

TAKE MY HAND!

HURRY!

DON'T **WORRY!** WE'VE **GOT** YOU!

NO--

--I'VE GOT YOU!

THIS WAY!

WHAT THE--?

WE... WE'RE STILL **HERE**...?

BUT WHERE IS "HERE"?

SOMEPLACE **BEYOND** THE BARRIERS OF **TIME** AND **SPACE**, BATMAN.

AN **ENTRYWAY** TO A REALM **UNACCUSTOMED** TO THE GAZE OF **MORTAL EYES**.

WHAT-- WHAT IS--?

HYPERTIME. THE VAST, INTERCONNECTED WEB OF *PARALLEL TIME-LINES* WHICH COMPRISE ALL REALITY.

I BELIEVE IT IS THE GREATEST SECRET IN ALL CREATION. GOG'S MASTERS GRANTED HIM MORE POWER THAN THEY REALIZED. IN HIS MADNESS, HE WAS ABLE TO SHATTER HYPERTIME'S BOUNDARIES.

HE THOUGHT HE WAS OMNIPOTENT.

BUT AS HE WILL SOON *LEARN*, IF HE HASN'T *ALREADY*...

... THE POSSIBILITIES OF *HYPERTIME* ARE INFINITE... AND HUMBLE THE POWER OF ANY MAN.

I SPENT MY *ENTIRE* LIFE SEARCHING FOR SUCH POSSIBILITIES. I *HAD* TO, BECAUSE...

...WELL... THAT'S A STORY FOR ANOTHER TIME.

BUT THE *LINEAR MEN*... THEY'VE TOLD US OVER AND OVER AGAIN THAT *ALTERNATE TIMELINES* ARE A MYTH.

THEY *WOULD.* THE PROBLEM WITH THE *LINEAR MEN* IS THAT THEY'RE *TOO LINEAR.* THEY'RE *VESTED* IN ENFORCING AN *INFLEXIBLE* VIEW OF REALITY--

--WHICH IS WHY I'VE HAD TO *HIDE* THIS FROM THEM AND THEIR *ALLIES* -- TO KEEP IT *PROTECTED* UNTIL IT WAS SAFE TO *REVEAL.*

THEY THINK *ORDERLY, CATALOGUED* CONTINUITY IS PREFERABLE TO A *KINGDOM OF WONDER.*

THEIR SENSE OF *CONTROL* WOULD BE SPLINTERED BY THE TRUTH THAT THE *UNIVERSE* THEY OVERSEE IS ACTUALLY PART OF AN UNPREDICTABLE *MULTI-VERSE*...

...AN *INFINITE* REALM OF *PARALLEL WORLDS* WHERE REALITY AS *YOU* KNOW IT HAS TAKEN DIFFERENT TWISTS AND TURNS.

WHERE FALLEN ALLIES LIVE *ON*...WHERE TRAGEDIES CAN BE TURNED TO *TRIUMPH.*

WHAT-- WHAT IS--?

HYPERTIME. THE VAST, INTERCONNECTED WEB OF *PARALLEL TIME-LINES* WHICH COMPRISE ALL REALITY.

I BELIEVE IT IS THE GREATEST SECRET IN ALL CREATION. GOG'S MASTERS GRANTED HIM MORE POWER THAN THEY REALIZED. IN HIS MADNESS, HE WAS ABLE TO SHATTER HYPERTIME'S BOUNDARIES.

HE THOUGHT HE WAS OMNIPOTENT.

BUT AS HE WILL SOON LEARN, IF HE HASN'T *ALREADY...*

... THE POSSIBILITIES OF *HYPERTIME* ARE INFINITE... AND HUMBLE THE POWER OF ANY MAN.

I SPENT MY *ENTIRE* LIFE SEARCHING FOR SUCH POSSIBILITIES. I *HAD* TO, BECAUSE...

...WELL... THAT'S A STORY FOR ANOTHER TIME.

BUT THE *LINEAR MEN...* THEY'VE TOLD US OVER AND OVER AGAIN THAT *ALTERNATE TIMELINES* ARE A MYTH.

THEY *WOULD.* THE PROBLEM WITH THE *LINEAR MEN* IS THAT THEY'RE *TOO LINEAR.* THEY'RE *VESTED* IN ENFORCING AN INFLEXIBLE VIEW OF REALITY--

--WHICH IS WHY I'VE HAD TO *HIDE* THIS FROM THEM AND THEIR *ALLIES* -- TO KEEP IT *PROTECTED* UNTIL IT WAS *SAFE* TO REVEAL.

THEY THINK *ORDERLY, CATALOGUED* CONTINUITY IS PREFERABLE TO A *KINGDOM OF WONDER.*

THEIR SENSE OF *CONTROL* WOULD BE SPLINTERED BY THE TRUTH THAT THE *UNIVERSE* THEY OVERSEE IS ACTUALLY PART OF AN UNPREDICTABLE *MULTI-VERSE...*

...AN *INFINITE* REALM OF *PARALLEL WORLDS* WHERE REALITY AS *YOU* KNOW IT HAS TAKEN DIFFERENT *TWISTS* AND *TURNS.*

WHERE FALLEN ALLIES LIVE *ON...* WHERE TRAGEDIES CAN BE TURNED TO *TRIUMPH.*

JONATHAN...?

OUR TIME HERE HAS ENDED, OUR WORK HERE IS DONE, SAVE FOR ONE FINAL TASK.

WE DO INDEED FADE...NOT INTO OBLIVION, BUT INTO OUR OWN KINGDOMS...

...WHERE WE BELONG... WHERE WE'LL BE SAFE.

WILL WE BE ABLE TO FIND THIS PLACE AGAIN? EXPLORE HYPERTIME... NAVIGATE IT IF NEED BE?

THAT ROAD IS HARD AND FRAUGHT WITH PERIL, BUT I PROMISE YOU...

...YOUR UNDERSTANDING OF HYPERTIME IS JUST BEGINNING.

AND YOU?

WILL YOU BE REAL AND CERTAIN IN OUR FUTURE?

PERHAPS...

...AND PERHAPS NOT.

NOW MORE THAN EVER, YOU KNOW THE MAGIC OF IT ALL.

EACH AND EVERY ONE OF US...WE ARE ALL STORIES SIMPLY WAITING TO BE TOLD.

JUST IMAGINE.

WE... ...NOT EVEN WE FULLY KNEW.

ALL THESE MILLENNIA... TO HAVE BEEN SO SHORTSIGHTED AS TO THE VERY REALITY OVER WHICH WE CLAIMED SUPREME KNOWLEDGE...

...WHAT NOW ARE OUR RESPONSIBILITIES?

YOUR FIRST RESPONSIBILITY --

--IS TO THIS INNOCENT WHO WAS THE PUPPET OF YOUR ARROGANCE!

I COMMAND YOU TO REPAIR THE DAMAGE YOU HAVE DONE TO THIS MAN!

HOW DARE YOU SPEAK TO US LIKE --

HOW DARE YOU HAVE SO LITTLE REGARD FOR THE HUMANITY YOU EACH ONCE KNEW?

REDEEM THIS MAN -- OR FACE A WRATH THAT, I PROMISE YOU, WOULD STAGGER EVEN HIS.

AN EMPTY THREAT.

NO. SHE HAS EVERY RIGHT TO ADDRESS US IN THAT MANNER.

IN THE FACE OF ALL WE HAVE SEEN TODAY... ALL THE COURAGE AND ALL THE PROMISE... PERHAPS IT IS TIME WE LEARNED HUMILITY ANEW...

...AND REFORGED OUR BOND TO THE HUMAN RACE...

...FOR THE GLORY OF ITS TRUE IDENTITY HAS JUST BEGUN.

FOR ALL HE'D DONE, HE DESERVED HEAVEN... NOT PRISON.

BUT NOW, AT LONG LAST, HE KNOWS THIS ISN'T THE JAIL HE ONCE BELIEVED IT TO BE.

NOW HE KNOWS THERE'S A DOOR.

THERE'S A DOOR, EVEN IF HE'S NOT GOING TO USE IT.

NOT TODAY, ANYWAY.

A GATHERING OF HEROES...
FROM TITAN BOOKS

All Titan Books' graphic novels are available through most good bookshops or direct from Titan Books' mail order service. To order telephone 01 858 433 169, or contact Titan Books Subscriptions Department, Bowden House, 36 Northampton Road, Market Harborough, Leics, LE16 9HE, quoting the reference code specified on the publication information page at the front of the book.